The Bear Next Door

Denis Knight

Denis Knight

THE
BEAR NEXT DOOR

A Soviet Adventure

K Publications

Copyright © Denis Knight 2005
Illustrations © Michael Darling 2005
First published in 2005 by K Publications
Hilton, Bishops Tawton
Barnstaple, Devon EX32 0AX

Distributed by Gazelle Book Services Limited
Hightown, White Cross Mills, South Rd, Lancaster
England LA1 4XS

British Library Cataloguing in Publication Data
A catalogue record for this book is available from the
British Library

ISBN 0-9548328-0-9

Typeset by Amolibros, Milverton, Somerset
This book production has been managed by Amolibros
Printed and bound by T J International Ltd, Padstow, Cornwall,
UK

This novel is dedicated to the great Russian people, who have contributed so much towards our musical, cultural and artistic heritage.

My wife and I encountered many difficulties in our travels, but our abiding memory is of their friendship towards us, their generosity to strangers and, above all, their good-humoured support of one another in their endless battles with an inflexible Soviet authority.

To all this we pay tribute – it augurs well for the future.

Special thanks to Beryl, Jon and Peter for their help and encouragement, also to John Down for his valuable suggestions.

I am particularly grateful to Michael Darling, whose inspired illustrations have added a special flavour to our adventure.

Other works by the author:

Hors de Combat
Judas in the Orchard
Rainbow – a collection of poetry

To Joan, my lifelong comrade

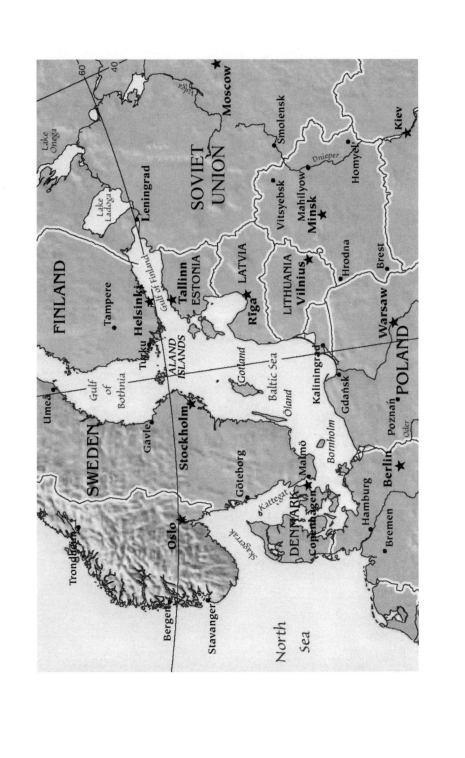

I blame John Richards for the whole thing.

John Richards, retired Master Baker, was respectably conservative—hardly the sort of person who'd go flying off to Soviet Russia in 1971 at the drop of a hat just because he loved Russian music and Russian ballet. He'd actually flown to Moscow twice that year so that he could be there, in the famous Bolshoi Theatre, at a time when most people still looked upon the Soviet Union with grave suspicion.

The Cold War was at its height and the Soviet Embassy sufficiently paranoid to sit on—and ultimately ignore—all enquiries from people who, for one reason or another, applied for visas to visit the Soviet Union, except of course for trade union officials travelling in organised groups, who were made doubly welcome and encouraged to spread the gospel on their return.

Into this morass of mutual suspicion plunged our friend. We knew he liked ballet, but it was a real eye-opener when we met him for lunch at the North Country Inn and he said he'd just got back from the Soviet Union. He produced a small Gladstone bag.

"Guess what's in here?"

We hadn't seen him for ages, but we'd heard rumours.

My wife, Joanna, the love of my life—a woman I could never control or even fully understand—was intrigued.

"Someone said you'd gone to Russia, but that was months ago."

"I know, but I couldn't resist the temptation to go again. When you reach my age, it's the things you haven't done you regret most. Besides, it was a lot easier the second time. The embassy knew who I was and the visa arrived in a few days instead of months and—not only that—when I arrived at the airport, a lovely young lady was waiting to greet me. She was holding a card with my name and she told me that she had an official car and driver waiting outside. She spoke perfect English and she said that the Ministry of Culture had authorised VIP treatment for my second visit. There was an official reception at the Bolshoi that afternoon with a gala performance afterwards. She whisked me off to my hotel and waited outside while I booked in and changed. The manager was bowing and scraping by this time, so she must have been someone fairly important.

"Then we raced off to the Bolshoi, where I was introduced as a ballet enthusiast, who had flown all the way from England for the second time this year, just to be with them. I was just on my third glass of champagne when the great Madame Greteskaya arrived. I recognised her immediately from my last visit and she too seemed to remember me, as she came across, shook me by the hand and presented me with a silver tie pin, which I've worn ever since. She said she'd come all the way from Leningrad to represent the Kirov.

"She thanked me for coming again: 'The Ministry of Culture are doing their best to promote the arts now and it's encouraging when friends like you come all this way to meet us twice in one year.'

"I stayed for a week and had the time of my life. The hotel bill was surprisingly modest and, as a VIP, I hardly paid for anything. They gave me tickets for every performance and I was usually invited backstage afterwards. I was really sorry to leave and several dancers came to the airport to see me off. I bought them all flowers and the biggest box of chocolates I could find and they gave me a small parcel at the last moment, which I opened as soon as we took off.

"I found a little note inside: 'Dear John, We have enjoyed so much your visit—here are some old Russian banknotes for you to paper your bedroom—they're no use now, so you might as well have them, then, every morning when you wake up, you'll think of us.' "

John upended the Gladstone bag and a shower of Russian banknotes cascaded on to the floor, old pre-revolution notes, with images of Tsars and dignitaries of the Russian Orthodox Church. We picked them up and spread them out on the table, where their bewhiskered faces stared blankly at the ceiling of the North Country Inn. He also had a large unopened envelope, sealed with the blue and gold crest of Leningrad.

"This was inside the parcel," he said. "I haven't opened it yet, but I'm sure it will ensure a hearty welcome to anyone who visits Leningrad and presents it to the Kirov. My travelling days are over now and you both love ballet, so I hope that, one day, you'll both make good use of the introduction."

He gave the envelope to Joanna and I realised then that I had very little choice. Joanna was hooked and I knew her well enough by now to realise that she wouldn't rest until we'd been to the Soviet Union—to the Kirov in Leningrad and the Bolshoi in Moscow. Not only that, but someone would have to paper the bedroom wall.

Things being what they were, it was another two years before we could even think about such an ambitious holiday. I stalled Joanna, who preferred motoring holidays, by promising that we would go to the Soviet Union as soon as they allowed tourists to take their own cars. This, at the time, seemed unlikely, to say the least, but, two years later, she read in the paper that, for the first time, tourists were now allowed to take their own cars to the Soviet Union.

That's why, in the autumn of 1973, we found ourselves, in the middle of the night, on our way to Tilbury.

One

The older I get, the easier it is to remember things that never happened.

It was September 1973 and the *Alexandr Pushkin*, flagship of the Baltic Steamship Line, lay alongside. She plied between Montreal and Leningrad during the summer months and she called at Tilbury to pick up passengers and supplies.

We arrived at the docks with our little car at the unearthly hour of six in the morning as instructed—three hours before departure. It was still quite dark and the huge liner loomed ominously, a giant shadow in the darkness. We drew up beside an ancient Hillman van and checked the time, just to make sure, then we locked up and went looking for a cafe. Breakfast it was, albeit greasy bacon and undrinkable coffee, but it warmed us up and gave us a bit of Dutch courage for the journey which lay ahead.

Things were beginning to move by the time we got back. Arc lights were shining and a huge lorry was parked at the dockside, its contents being checked by a man in uniform. He seemed to be the only official in sight, so we waited patiently until he returned to what was apparently his office, unlocked the door, switched on the light and locked the door again.

I knocked, nervously.

"Don't say you're here already—it'll be hours before anything happens. The driver can't speak a word of English, so how on earth can I be expected to sort out his bill of lading?—it's all in Russian anyway and, as if that wasn't bad enough—Cyrillic, too."

He buttoned his uniform, donned his official cap and sat down behind a desk. "Seeing you're here, we might as well make a start."

I handed him our passports and he gave a grunt of approval.

"At least you've taken the trouble to get visas—you'd be surprised how many hopeful travellers think they can just sail over to Leningrad and land, even after they've been warned they haven't a hope in hell. The Soviet authorities clamp down hard on anyone without a visa—they're not even allowed to leave the ship and they have to spend five days on the *Pushkin* at their own expense and another four days and nights after that before they eventually arrive back here with their tails between their legs."

He stamped our passports and examined our other papers.

"I must warn you that the green card isn't worth the paper it's written on, as the Soviet authorities don't recognise any of our insurance policies. Here's a copy of their present regulations concerning compulsory insurance cover for foreigners."

He handed us an important-looking document.

"But...it's all in Russian."

"All I have, I'm afraid. We did hand out translations three years ago when visitors to the Soviet Union were allowed to bring their own cars, but they changed the rules last summer and impounded so many cars for real or imaginary transgressions it took us several months to sort it all out."

He returned Yoddy's registration book and green insurance card.

"Not that they're any use where you're going, but I see you're returning overland through Poland and East Germany and you'll be glad to hear that both those countries now recognise our own insurance cards."

We thanked him for his help and turned to leave.

"One further point," he said, "make sure the crane driver knows your car has to be loaded aboard the *Pushkin*. I have a copy of the manifest here and it would seem there is only one other car for Leningrad—a white Hillman van—so you should park your car next to the Hillman to be on the safe side. They left a car behind once and, understandably, the owner wasn't exactly overjoyed when he went up on deck and found his car wasn't there."

Joanna looked at me accusingly: "You never told me about this."

"How could I?" I remonstrated. "It's hardly the sort of thing they publicise."

"Doesn't matter anyway, we'll soon be on our way to Leningrad."

"Yes," I added, "secure in the knowledge that everyone in the Kirov is simply dying to meet us."

She looked at me suspiciously.

"If that's your idea of sarcasm, this is hardly the best time to score cheap points."

Suitably chastened, I took her arm and we walked the full length of the ship towards Yoddy. Joanna had insisted from the start that our almost new little car would be called Yoddy and, when Joanna made up her mind about something, who was I to disagree? The giant liner towered above us. Lights were streaming through her portholes and people were moving about on deck. The illustrated brochure from the Black Sea and Baltic Steamship Company had given us an indication of her beauty, but nothing had prepared us for such a magnificent cruise liner when we had booked passage to Leningrad.

"What a beautiful ferry," sighed Joanna, extremely impressed.

"No ferry," I said, "more like a luxury cruise liner— we're going on a four-day cruise to Leningrad. I arranged it as a surprise to get our holiday off to a good start."

I might have added that it was the Soviet embassy who had insisted on our booking passage on the *Pushkin* before they sent us an entry visa. There were of course other ways of getting to Leningrad, but the thought of driving the best part of a thousand miles through East Germany and Poland before we even arrived in the Soviet Union was indeed somewhat daunting, so perhaps they had a point.

Joanna squeezed my arm in gratitude and I was off the hook.

Yoddy was still where we'd left her, but there was an official-looking notice on her windscreen.

"Wonder what that's all about?"

"Haven't a clue, let's see if that white van has one as well."

"Perhaps they're parking tickets."

We hung around, waiting for something to happen.

10

"Wonder where the driver is?"

As if in answer to Joanna's question, a cheerful, middle-aged man bounded down some steps and greeted us.

"So you're the owners of this tarty new car—thought you'd turn up sooner or later. Glad to meet two fellow travellers, though I must warn you that no one seems to have a clue what's going on—I'm Wally Merilaht, by the way."

He held out his hand and we introduced ourselves.

"I'm Denis," I told him, "and this is my wife, Joanna, the love of my life."

"Shut up," said Joanna, smiling.

"I've been waiting three years—three bloody years, mind you," cursed Wally in a strong Welsh accent, "for a visa to visit my old mother in Tallinn. I'd almost given up hope of ever seeing her again, when, three weeks ago, the visa suddenly arrived in the post—without any warning, mind you, so I had to get a move on."

"How did you manage to arrange everything so quickly?" I asked. "It took us well over three months and they never replied to any of our letters, so we didn't know until last week whether we'd be allowed to come or not."

"Ah, that's typical," he replied, "but I have an advantage, see—I'm Russian myself so I know the way they think—and another thing, I can talk to them in their own language. Most of them never bother about anything except their bellies, so I told them my mother was dying and they'd better arrange for me to travel on the *Pushkin* straightaway or they'd have the *Daily Mirror* on the phone for comments on my letter about the callous and unfeeling officials in the Soviet Embassy."

"That's the way to deal with them," asserted Joanna, looking at me. "You should be more assertive."

"Glad you speak Russian," I said to Wally. "Perhaps you could translate that notice on my windscreen."

"Easy, boyo—it says 'cars with an L on the roof will be loaded before departure'."

"What happens to the others?" I asked, but he seemed singularly unconcerned.

"I suppose they're left behind."

"How about our car?"

"Haven't you put an L on your roof yet?—you'd better watch it, boyo, before the crane driver gets here. Where's your bit of chalk?"

"I haven't got any chalk."

"Didn't that man give you a bit?"

"What man?"

"The man in the little hut up there."

This was getting ridiculous.

"I didn't even know he was there—how could I possibly have known?"

"You could have used your eyes, boyo."

Joanna started to giggle and I knew he was having me on.

"Tell you what," I suggested. "All is forgiven if you'll lend me your piece of chalk."

"Don't know about that—might need it myself."

They hooted with laughter and the tensions of the past few hours melted away. Good old Wally—he would make all the difference on the cruise and, for the first time that morning, I began to enjoy myself.

"All you have to do," said Wally, "is to go up those steps and into that little cabin and ask the chap inside for a sticker—or even a piece of chalk if you prefer. He'll charge you fifty new pence—better give him a pound or he might only let you have a piece of chalk."

I climbed the wooden steps with as much dignity as I could muster.

"On second thoughts," he shouted, "better give him two pounds—you never know when you'll need his help. All sorts of things could happen before we sail—the crane driver could drop your car into the sea and an independent witness might be useful."

I treated this information with the contempt it deserved, but, annoyingly, Joanna was still laughing. "Careful," I shouted to her, "remember—many a true word is spoken in jest."

I knocked on the door of the wooden hut and it was only then I saw a notice in English—'Drivers Report Here'. The lettering was so small that it was almost invisible from the ground, but Wally, Mr Knowall, must have seen it as soon as he arrived. Sooner or later, I would have to curb his warped sense of humour, which seemed to reduce Joanna to helpless laughter.

A nondescript little man was sitting at a table. He had a notebook and a small pile of plastic stickers in front of him.

"Passports, please."

He examined our visas carefully.

"Fifty new pence, please."

I handed over fifty pence and helped myself to a plastic sticker, but he'd obviously finished with me. Fifty pence was all he asked for, so that's what he got. So much for Wally's stupid advice.

I walked down the steps with as much dignity as I could

muster, clutching my square of white self-adhesive plastic with a large black L in the middle.

"There, I told you so," said Wally. "I can't understand how on earth you thought chalk would do the trick—what with the spray and the rain, it wouldn't even last the first day."

"It wouldn't have to," I retorted. "The cars will be loaded in no time and it won't matter then whether the stickers are there or not. Come to think of it, how d'you know the plastic won't strip the paint off the roofs of our cars? It wouldn't matter in your case of course—the paint's peeling off already."

"That's enough, you two," intervened Joanna. "Time you concentrated on doing something useful instead of scoring cheap points all the time. We've all had a good laugh now and the crane driver's already in his cab, waiting for the dockers to arrive."

As she spoke, a tractor and trailer drew up and four men unloaded a makeshift cradle.

"Are these the two cars?"

Without waiting for an answer, they told Wally to take the handbrake off and manhandled his ancient van on to their cradle, then the foreman blew a whistle and the crane driver lowered a huge hook. In no time at all they'd secured the van in the cradle, the foreman blew his whistle and, with astonishing speed, the little van, shot up into the air and disappeared over the stern of the *Pushkin*.

Yoddy's turn next. I held up my plastic sticker, but the foreman brushed it aside.

"Wretched things," he muttered. "More trouble than they're worth. They keep falling off, then they blame us for rough handling—beats me why drivers can't stay with their own cars until they're safely loaded. Stand back, young man, while we bounce your car on to the cradle."

As he spoke, the empty cradle whistled down and crashed to the ground beside them.

"Good lad, that one—knows exactly what he's doing to the nearest twelve inches—nearly had my head off once when I was standing a bit too close and it upset him so much that I had to take him down to the pub and buy him a pint to steady his nerves."

I watched anxiously while they bounced Yoddy into her cradle.

Yoddy, our pride and joy and a beauty if there ever was one, was lifted up, secured tightly and launched into space at the speed of light. We watched apprehensively as she flew towards the *Pushkin* and disappeared over the stern.

"Happy landing, dear," shouted Joanna.

Her sudden disappearance had taken us by surprise and we looked around for Wally, who was nowhere to be seen.

"Probably hurrying up the gang plank to ingratiate himself with the captain," said Joanna.

It was quite a climb to the top deck. We presented our tickets and were delighted to find that we had a first-class cabin on the upper deck.

Joanna was ecstatic. "Why didn't you tell me we had a first-class cabin?"

One didn't have to do anything wrong to be accused by Joanna—doing something right without telling her could be equally hazardous, unless of course it was a surprise. I remembered reading somewhere about Soviet railway carriages, which, in keeping with equality, had abolished

15

first and second class in favour of 'soft class' and 'hard class'.

"I remember now." My voice was triumphant. "First class cabins are referred to as soft class, but I didn't realise what that meant until after we'd booked."

"So that's why the ferry cost so much?"

"Cruise liner, you mean."

"Cruise liner or ferry, doesn't matter—we're here and we've got a lovely cabin."

She kissed me and I knew we were off to a promising start.

"Real bath, too—quick, fetch the suitcases from the car while I see if the water's hot enough."

I went out on deck to fetch the cases and there was Yoddy safe and sound, just round the corner. Wally was standing nearby, deep in conversation with a tall, distinguished looking man in his early fifties, smoking a cigar—perhaps he was the captain.

"Denis—I'd like to introduce you to my new friend, Aram. He's a dental surgeon from Armenia and he's on his way home from Canada, where he's been attending a dental congress."

How on earth did Wally to get to know people well enough to call them by their first name almost immediately? Who were these privileged Russians, apparently able to come and go at the drop of a hat in the middle of the Cold War?—and who were all those other people wandering around the ship? Aram explained that most of them were second and third generation Russian families. Their parents and grandparents had fled to the New World after the revolution and they were now returning to the uncertainties of the Soviet Union—not only that,

16

but returning in sufficient numbers to persuade the Soviet authorities to divert a profitable cruise liner to the less profitable Atlantic crossings.

Aram the dental surgeon, the privileged one, able, apparently, to attend international conferences at will— he would know all about them. I was on the point of asking him when a loud blast from the funnel heralded our departure. We went across to the rail to wave goodbye and I looked at my watch—twelve noon exactly. Joanna and I had been hanging around for six hours and she probably needed a drink as much as I did—and lunch as well, if we could find the dining room.

Aram must have guessed what I was thinking.

"Why don't we meet in the bar for a mid-morning aperitif?"

He spoke perfect English, with just a hint of an American accent.

"Not for me," said Wally, "I haven't even found my cabin yet—somewhere in the steerage I expect."

He took a battered-looking suitcase from the back of his van and left us to it, but I hesitated, remembering Joanna waiting for her bath.

Aram looked at his watch: "I've got a better idea. Why don't you and your wife join me for lunch? Mr Merilaht happened to mention that this was your first trip to the Soviet Union, so it will be my pleasure to introduce you to our gastronomic delights. Make the most of them while you're on the *Pushkin*— you're unlikely to find anything quite so special when you get to Leningrad."

"Thank you so much," I replied. "I'm sure my wife will be delighted to join us, but she's waiting for me to collect our cases from the car so she can have a bath and change."

"So this is your car—this lovely little Toyota next to Mr Merilaht's rather ancient van. I do hope it survives the journey to Tallinn."

"Surely Tallinn isn't that far from Leningrad?"

"You obviously don't know our roads. I won't disillusion him, but Merilaht will be fortunate indeed if he gets there all in one piece."

He helped me out with the suitcases and showed me where the restaurant was.

"There's one on every deck, but ours is far superior—first class passengers only. So much for equality. I'll stay put now I'm here and order lunch for three."

Back in our cabin, I broke the good news to Joanna.

"You can't be serious, how on earth can I be expected to get ready in half an hour?"

The usual arguments, even on holiday.

"How about forty-five minutes?"

She was ready on time and we hurried along the top deck to the restaurant.

Aram was there of course, drink in hand.

"So this is your beautiful wife?—delighted to meet you, Madame."

The old charmer—kissing her hand, too.

"Your husband and I have been getting to know each other. We have four clear days ahead and I do hope you will do me the honour of lunching with me each day to enable me to introduce you to our finest Russian cuisine before we arrive in Leningrad."

How very embarrassing, we couldn't possibly afford to repay such lavish hospitality.

18

I had a sudden idea.

"Perhaps you would allow us to pay for the drinks?"

He shrugged and was about to protest, then changed his mind.

"Well—if you insist."

The waiter handed us the wine list. It was printed in Russian, so the choice had to be Aram's.

"They have some fine Georgian wines," he said, "so perhaps, as this is a special occasion, we might choose this one, but I would like to mention that they do an excellent house wine and we could, if you wish, experiment with that tomorrow."

I looked at him gratefully—he obviously realised we wouldn't want to squander hard-earned holiday money too soon and this was his way of avoiding embarrassment.

We had an excellent meal and I decided to take the opportunity of getting to know him better. There was so much we needed to know about the Soviet Union and he was just the right person to advise us how best to avoid some of the difficulties that might lie ahead.

We had a coffee and a cognac and I asked him if he would like to join us later.

"Give us an hour or so to straighten up, then come round—cabin sixty-three."

"Delighted!" came the reply. "I haven't far to come— my cabin's number seventy."

I made a mental note to watch him like a hawk. Joanna might well respond to a shipboard flirtation and I could see by the way he looked at her that he was hoping for just that.

"Thanks again for the invitation," he said. "I'll be with you in about an hour."

19

"We haven't got any wine or anything," hissed Joanna.

"We soon will," I replied.

I gave the waiter a tip and had a quick word with him about Aram's impending visit.

"Thank you, Comrade. I couldn't help overhearing part of your conversation, so I would like to suggest Doctor Kuryokhin's favourite Georgian champagne. He travels with us frequently and he'll be delighted to share your bottle of cognac. The waitress will bring it to your cabin, with three glasses, in about ten minutes."

This was a lucky break, as we now knew Aram's full name without having to ask. We cleaned up the cabin and made a list of things we wanted to know, then Aram arrived and we opened the cognac.

"My favourite!" he exclaimed. "How on earth did you know?—oh, the waiter of course—I shall have to reprimand him."

Joanna started the ball rolling. She produced her precious letter of introduction to Madame Greteskaya and handed it to him.

"It's probably all in Russian," she said. "My friend in England gave it to me—it's a letter of introduction to a lady who is well known in the world of Russian ballet."

Aram opened the letter and began to read.

"Good heavens," he shouted suddenly, "have you any idea how important Madame Greteskaya is?—she's the 'grande dame' of Russian ballet—the equivalent of your own Madame Rambert. We must drink a toast immediately."

He drained his glass in one gulp and sat down heavily.

"You won't find her in Leningrad," he said. "She and her partner have been banished to Moscow. They are still greatly loved and admired, but—let me put it this way—

there is an old Chinese curse, many thousands of years old—'May you come to the attention of those in authority'. Since our revolution, 'those in authority' have become more numerous and more powerful and it is now unwise for anyone, no matter how famous, to draw attention to themselves in case the authorities decide to clip their wings. The Russian people have been pushed around by the Czars and the monks and the landlords for hundreds of years and they're now being pushed around by the commissars. Madame Greteskaya and her partner must have stepped out of line once too often. Everyone is up in arms, but there's nothing we can do about it—it's an absolute disgrace."

He became quite agitated, so we poured him another glass.

"I must apologise for this unseemly display of emotion, but nearly everyone in the public eye lives on a knife edge—and it's all so unnecessary."

He seemed to know quite a lot about the world of Soviet ballet and we waited eagerly for him to continue.

"Russian ballet is world famous and those who create it by writing the music and dedicating their lives to dancing and the theatre are free spirits, so they are the very people who find it difficult to conform to Soviet ideology. The authorities therefore have an image problem. On the one hand, they value the prestige and the financial returns which stem from the worldwide reputation of the Kirov, but, on the other hand, they resent their freedom to travel outside the Soviet Union, without which Soviet ballet would soon cease to be of international importance. Add to this the continuing rivalry which exists between the Kirov in Leningrad and the Bolshoi in Moscow and you have a situation where the bureaucrats in Moscow may find the Bolshoi easier to control—and you can guess the rest."

"How about writers and artists?" asked Joanna. "Are they controlled too?"

"Yes, unfortunately, although, being less in the public eye, they sometimes manage to obtain exit visas to attend conferences, and so on."

"How about doctors and dental surgeons?"

"Ah, that would be telling—perhaps the answer to that particular question should wait until tomorrow. I've greatly enjoyed our little discussion, but you will want time to yourselves and I mustn't overstay my welcome. Perhaps you will permit me to return the compliment by inviting you to my cabin tomorrow afternoon, where we can sample genuine Stolichnaya vodka, which, by the way, travels freely to capitalist countries without the restrictions which the rest of us find so irksome."

He rose to his feet and kissed Joanna's hand.

"Madame, it has been my pleasure to meet such a charming and intelligent lady and I hope we can all meet for lunch tomorrow—would one o'clock suit you?"

I could see that Joanna was almost purring.

"Quite a charmer," she said after he'd left.

"Steady girl, best not complicate things, you can see what he's up to."

"I know," was her rueful response, "but he really is charming."

We met Wally that evening and spent an enjoyable couple of hours, though not at the captain's table as he'd promised. "These things take time," he said, "but I've had a word with him and he's going to show me his Cadillac tomorrow morning—it's under wraps next to my van."

I hadn't realised until then there was a third car on board, loaded at Montreal presumably, and I wondered who the fortunate owner was. It must have cost a small fortune to bring it all the way from Canada—perhaps a friend of the captain's, bucking the system. It did cross my mind that the car might belong to our smooth-talking friend, but even he was unlikely to be able to afford a vintage Cadillac.

I went out on deck early the following morning. It was a breezy morning with plenty of spray, but a few passengers were already admiring Yoddy, so I lifted her bonnet and the more knowledgeable among them discussed the finer points of advanced Japanese engineering. Other onlookers were waiting patiently for a glimpse of the wonderful American Cadillac, which had remained covered for the voyage across the Atlantic.

The captain soon arrived, accompanied by Aram. They untied the wraps and there, for all to see, was a sight for sore eyes—a magnificent car if ever there was one.

Aram spoke first.

"The captain and I," he said, "share an enthusiasm for old cars. This car belongs to a wealthy Russian living in Montreal, who entrusted her to him before we left and begged him to ensure that she was delivered safely to her new owner in Leningrad. This is the first opportunity we've had to make sure that all is well."

They checked the logbook against the customs documents, then they opened her huge bonnet, primed the engine and swung the starting handle. She started first time, sweet as a nut, and I was glad to feel that Yoddy was in such good company.

I helped them replace the wraps and Wally joined us in the bar for coffee.

"So this is where you go," he said, "while proles like me have to be content with lesser facilities—so much for equality."

The captain looked sheepish, but Aram shrugged his shoulders.

"Equality," he told us, "as we have found to our cost, is relative. Despite our dreams of a better society, we have found that true equality is probably unattainable. The late George Orwell, himself a disenchanted Communist, said as much in his novel *Animal Farm*, where the pigs, having helped overthrow the tyrannical farmer in a bloodless coup, announced that they were now in charge and propounded the revolutionary slogan that, from now on, all animals were equal, although some were more equal than others. Unfortunately, our own revolution has left the pigs in charge, so we have to survive as best we can. Those who now rule us have decided in their wisdom to divert a profitable cruise liner from the Caribbean to this dreary Atlantic crossing. They doubtless have their reasons, but the fact remains that these political decisions have to be paid for by people more equal than others— myself for instance—who are able to travel to and fro. It's our money which enables the proles, as you call them, to take advantage of the excellent facilities provided on this liner."

Good old Aram, never at a loss for words.

The captain, lacking his fluency, was content, and even Wally seemed to agree.

We'd never been on a luxury cruise liner before and the *Pushkin* was a real beauty. The crew were obviously hand-picked and couldn't have been more helpful. Aram was a mine of useful information, though he never gave much away about himself. He introduced us to several Russian families who, after many years in Canada and America, were returning to the Soviet Union. Most of them were just looking forward to going home, but one family we met had a more compelling reason.

"It's like this 'ere, bud, if you was a New York garbage collector and your father was one too and you looked at your son and you knew, just knew, he'd grow up to be one as well, then you'd always be thinking that one day—maybe one day when things got a bit better at home—you'd be able to go home at last, then you heard this year that things at home really were getting better and you read about a special offer of cheap travel home for your family, what would you do? All I did was ring the Soviet Consulate in Montreal and they put me through to the Black Sea & Baltic booking agent. He said he'd send me a form and they'd do the rest, so I waited for the form to arrive and sent it back with a cheque for a few hundred dollars—and here we are, less than six months later, travelling in style and looking forward to going home at last."

He had a copy of a Russian language magazine published in Canada. It had several interesting articles and photographs on life in the Soviet Union, so it was hardly surprising that second- and third-generation Russians, longing for their homeland, would seize the opportunity to return on assisted passages to test the temperature, their only commitment being to remain for twelve months, after which, should they so wish, they could return on assisted passages.

We were offered a beginner's course in Russian, including an introduction to the Cyrillic alphabet. The very thought of having to learn the Cyrillic alphabet intimidated me to such an extent that I declined their kind offer, although Joanna decided to have a go. Her teacher was one of the ship's officers, a buxom young lady, and I nearly changed my mind when I saw her, but decided instead to enjoy the freedom of the *Pushkin* while I had the chance, secure in the knowledge that Aram was hardly likely to pounce while Joanna was having Russian lessons.

We awoke on our last morning to the unforgettable sight of the beautiful golden spire of Leningrad's Peter-Paul Cathedral, shimmering in the distant haze. We were soon entering Leningrad harbour and I went out on deck to gaze in wonder at this Venice of the North, founded by Peter the Great in 1703 on the marshlands of the River Neva and destined to become Russia's gateway to the west. Joanna soon joined me. She was clutching an official-looking parchment scroll, which, she explained, was her certificate of competence in the Russian alphabet.

"There," she said; "from now on, you will consult me whenever we have a problem with the Cyrillic alphabet. It has thirty-two letters, making Russian a very expressive language—when making love, for instance. What a pity we have to part from our new friends so soon."

"Meaning Wally, of course?"

"Him too, though I actually had the old smoothie in mind—rather more interesting."

"How about me for a change?"

The *Pushkin* edged slowly into the inner harbour, giving a long blast to announce her arrival. Other ships responded in a chorus of greeting for their flagship, returned safely from the perils of the New World, her holds stuffed with much needed machine tools in exchange for their own exports of Stolichnaya and caviar.

On board were their own Comrades, returning at last to their homeland. Not only families, but officials who had been expelled from the Soviet Embassy in New York and more than a sprinkling of commercial spies, who, according to Aram, travelled to and fro with the full knowledge of all concerned. The machine tools were important, relying as they did on the greed of American entrepreneurs, who, for many years, had been obtaining export licences for Canada and arranging for the tools to be stored in the Black Sea & Baltic warehouse in Montreal until the *Pushkin*'s monthly trip to the Soviet Union. Payment would be made in roubles, deposited in a Montreal bank and in due course exchanged for American dollars, which eventually found their way to the manufacturers in payment for their special Canadian exports.

As for the Stolichnaya and caviar, these were merely sweeteners to encourage the middlemen involved.

Joanna snorted.

"I suppose the old smoothie told you this—sounds like a lot of nonsense to me."

"Me too, but you never know—the machine tools alone would make the crossing well worthwhile—anyway, it makes a good story."

We watched as the engines reversed and the *Pushkin*

inched gently inwards. Ropes were fastened and we were safely home at last. Gangways were lowered and an army of officials swarmed aboard, watched by the fifty or so workers who were apparently needed to berth such a large vessel—labour intensive with a vengeance.

Aram joined us at the rail.

"Just look at that—do you know how many men they need to berth the *Pushkin* in Montreal? Believe it or not—only eight men to do exactly the same job—and I expect it's the same in Germany. We've a long way to go before we can compete with them."

"Think about it," I said. "Isn't it better to employ men who would otherwise have nothing to do? It gives them a sense of purpose if you encourage them to do something useful instead of hanging around, doing nothing."

"You're probably right," conceded Aram, "but remember—we're competing with American efficiency and we just can't afford the luxury of employing forty or more layabouts to do nothing all day, however admirable the principle."

Two

Martial music interrupted our conversation and the captain's voice came over the tannoy, loud and clear.

"Will all passengers who are leaving the ship please collect their passports and entry visas from the first class dining room on the upper deck."

A large banner at the entrance welcomed us to the Union of Soviet Socialist Republics and the welcoming committee stood around to greet us, together with a few suspicious-looking officials, sitting at tables, with piles of passports, visas and landing cards spread out in front of them.

We formed an orderly queue and awaited our turn.

"I understand you have on board a car—a Japanese car."

I detected a note of disapproval.

"And this lady is your wife?"

No disapproval here—Joanna's dazzling smile, guaranteed to disarm anyone.

"I see you plan to spend one week in Leningrad and two weeks in Moscow. How about the rest of your holiday?"

"We're not sure yet—Intourist told us to contact them as soon as we arrived in Moscow and they would arrange accommodation for our fourth week, which would include our return journey through Poland and East Germany."

"Quite so—tourists are now permitted to travel through Poland and the DDR. They will arrange for you to spend one night in Smolensk, one in Minsk and, subject to the consent of the Polish authorities, one or two nights in Warsaw. I wish you a pleasant journey and hope you enjoy the Kirov ballet in Leningrad and the Bolshoi in Moscow."

How did they know about our plans to visit the ballet? Perhaps Aram was a police informer on the side and that was how he was able to entertain so lavishly. I said as much to Joanna, but she pooh-poohed the idea.

"He gave too much away," she pointed out. "We've got enough on him to have him sent to Siberia."

"What's this I hear about Siberia?"

Aram again, hovering just behind us.

Joanna turned to face him.

"We were wondering," she said, bold as brass. "Perhaps you're a police informer."

"Wish I was sometimes," he replied, cool as a cucumber. "The trouble is that police informers are here today and gone tomorrow, while I, on the other hand, am here to stay. As a matter of fact, I only came to say goodbye and to wish you both a pleasant journey. We may meet again when we go through customs, but, if we don't, may I say what a pleasure it has been to meet you both."

We shook hands and he gave Joanna a farewell kiss.

"I shall always remember you my dear," he said—and then he was gone, like a thief in the night.

Joanna and I glanced at each other. Was it my imagination or did she give me a wink? We were shepherded down the gang plank before I had a chance to make up my mind and we waited patiently for Yoddy to be offloaded.

The captain strolled towards us and I assumed he was waiting for the Cadillac until I spied the ubiquitous Aram, still hovering, but discreetly, waiting for what? The captain stopped beside him and they shook hands as if in farewell.

"Look," said Joanna, "there's something going on over there; Aram's giving him money, lots of money, and they're counting it as fast as they can."

Then, casually, the captain strolled towards one of the customs officials and spoke to him. The man nodded and, as soon as the Cadillac was offloaded, he got behind the wheel and, with Aram sitting beside him, drove towards the customs shed.

Yoddy came next, so we followed them for a few hundred yards, with Wally close behind us. We parked and awaited our turn until the back door of the customs shed swung open and the Cadillac reappeared, with Aram driving. He waved us in and, once in the shed, we stood and watched while poor Yoddy was given a thorough going-over. Everything was taken out and examined, even her spare wheel, while our cases and bags were thoroughly searched.

One book nearly proved our undoing—*Short Stories by Russian Authors*, which we had brought with us to create a good impression and help us on our way. This, for some reason, was seized upon in triumph and taken to an inside room and we waited apprehensively until an officer in full military uniform came out and returned it with a flourish.

"Congratulations," he said. "It's nice to meet visitors who appreciate our Russian authors."

The back door opened and we were waved on, but not before Wally's van appeared, trailing black smoke. He told us afterwards that the customs officers were so delighted to meet a fellow Russian that they seemed to forget completely why he was there. After the black smoke had cleared, they looked at his old van and asked him if he'd bought a Russian van by mistake. He said that he certainly wasn't going to wait for three years and pay well over the odds for an equally dreadful Russian van. This remark caused them considerable amusement and, roaring with laughter, they poured him a glass of vodka and waved him on without even searching his luggage.

"They even gave me a push to help me on my way," he laughed. "Then they carried on slurping their vodka as if nothing had happened."

We stood there, wondering what to do next. Even Aram, the confident one, didn't seem to know.

"You may not realise it," he said, "but the Leningrad dock complex is a prohibited area, which means we shouldn't really be here at all. Permission has to be obtained before anyone can enter and even the captain's movements are restricted. He's on the *Pushkin* now, keeping an eye on the passengers who are spending their last night on board—immigrants mostly, but with a few Canadian tourists on package holidays and the usual sprinkling of spies and disgraced embassy officials, thrown out of America. It would probably be better to leave the cars here and walk back to the *Pushkin*, where we can get everything we need to comply with the numerous regulations lying in wait for us as soon as we leave the dock area."

"Such as?"

"Compulsory car insurance for instance. Set one foot, or, to be more precise, two of Yoddy's wheels outside the dock gates without insurance and you'll be in serious trouble—they might even confiscate her on the spot—then where would you be? You also have to buy roubles at a ridiculous exchange rate of two, three or even four roubles to the dollar when the actual rate is nearer eight—but watch out for the black marketeers, who will offer you much more—they're being watched all the time and, if anyone's caught doing a deal, the tourist is fined a hundred roubles on the spot and the black marketeer is imprisoned. Then there are vouchers, which have to be purchased before you can do anything—hotel and breakfast vouchers—and petrol coupons (buy the maximum each day, else you won't have enough to get you to Moscow), then there are ballet tickets, but you can buy these at your hotel if you prefer—they have a daily allocation of good seats for their guests—and all that's just for starters."

"Dear me," said Joanna. "It all sounds very complicated."

"You haven't heard the half of it yet—want me to continue?"

"No thanks, that's enough for the time being."

We walked to the *Pushkin* and spent what seemed like hours in filling up forms, changing money and queuing for the various scraps of paper without which we would undoubtedly have been arrested long before we had even reached our hotel. At last, exhausted by all the paperwork, we were ready to go. We filed down the gangway, but, when the cars came in sight, we saw to our dismay that a Swedish-registered black Volvo was there, parked beside them. Not only that, but the cars were surrounded by customs officers and a military police officer was striding up and down. Even at that distance, he seemed extremely irritated.

As we drew closer, he looked up, saw us coming and advanced towards us.

"Trouble ahead, I fear," muttered Aram.

We put a bold face on it and, smiling, greeted him cheerily.

The police officer spoke first.

"Are these your cars?" he asked crossly.

"That's right," said Wally, in Russian, "All except your black Volvo."

The police officer bristled.

"I'll have you know, gentlemen, that the black Volvo does not belong to me, so it is quite obvious that it must belong to one of you. You are reminded that the illegal import of foreign cars is a criminal offence and I hereby detain you all, including the lady, on suspicion of collusion in the importation of a foreign car until such time as a confession is forthcoming. Kindly come with me."

He led the way into the customs shed and we followed him into a little room at the side. He examined our documents and finally spoke rapidly in Russian and in German.

"I'm afraid we shall have to detain you all until the culprit confesses."

"How...how long will that take?"

"All night if necessary."

Joanna whispered to me.

"How about a loo?" I asked.

"There's a toilet here, I think."

The police officer opened a door next to the washbasin and peered inside.

34

"Just a small one, but better than nothing."

"Not for me it isn't."

Joanna spoke for the first time and the police officer hesitated, not just because he was speaking to a woman, but, deprived of German, the language of authority, he now had no choice but to speak in English, the language of moderation.

Having joined the fray, Joanna followed up with a left hook.

"I am a British citizen and I demand to know why I have been arrested."

"With respect, madam, you have not been arrested, neither have you been charged with any offence—I am merely detaining you here on suspicion that you might be involved in a felony."

"Felony?—what felony?"

The police officer sighed. If only he'd gone home sooner.

"I demand to see my friend, Madame Greteskaya."

Aram was impressed—even he couldn't have done better.

The police officer gulped. Everyone in Leningrad knew Madame Greteskaya and he certainly didn't want any more trouble.

"That will not be possible at the moment," he said, "but I'll contact my superiors straightaway, the ones who make the decisions, and they may decide to release you and your husband on bail, so you may not have to spend the night here. The captain of the *Pushkin* has already vouched for you and, as soon as we've fingerprinted the car and forced the locks, we will find out who the culprit is and you will then be free to leave."

"That's better," said Joanna. Her face was flushed, but she'd made her point.

"Now about this toilet…"

"Please, madam, I do realise that, from your point of view, sharing a toilet with three men may be less than satisfactory, but I feel the most important thing at the moment is for me to contact my superior officer so that we may take whatever action is necessary to bring this unfortunate matter to a satisfactory conclusion."

He clicked his heels and strode away, locking the door behind him.

"I'm thirsty," said Joanna, "let's see if there's anything to drink."

There was a small refrigerator in the corner and, predictably, several bottles of vodka.

"We're in luck," said Aram, "it's Stolichnaya, probably confiscated from some poor sod trying to evade duty—six bottles too."

"How about food?"

Wally of course—who else?

"It's all very well for you to look at me like that—bloody capitalists, wining and dining in style while I've been practically starving in the steerage—talk about equality."

We found some newly baked bread and an unopened crate of salami—someone had obviously been planning a feast—then, joy of joys, a saucepan full of borsch.

"For the benefit of the uninitiated," announced Aram, "borsch is a vegetable soup. It is made with beetroot and cabbage."

"All right, clever clogs, stop airing your superior knowledge."

"You've foxed me at last," said Aram, "what is a clever clog?"

"Haven't a clue."

We laughed, Comrades in adversity.

The meal was a huge success. We all went to the toilet afterwards and even Joanna didn't complain—in fact, under the influence of the vodka, she soon began to giggle and I knew, at least for the time being, that all was well.

"Jush you wait till we get home," she announced proudly. "I shall tell everyone that you made me shpend the night in a police cell in Leningrad with three strange men and my friend Madame Greteskaya came to my rescue and saved me from a fate worse than death."

She ran out of steam after that, so I made her comfortable on a blanket in the corner and she fell asleep almost immediately.

"Now," I said to the others, "let's come clean and tell each other who we think is responsible for all this."

We looked straight at Aram. He was the one with the secrets, the one who might even be responsible for our present predicament.

"Let's draw lots," said Aram. "The one who can toss an empty vodka glass at that crate in the corner so that it lands on the top of the crate and stays there is the winner."

"The winner of what?"

"The winner is the one who decides who is to speak first."

Just as well that Joanna's asleep, I thought, else I'd never hear the last of this nonsense. As for Aram, he'd obviously done this trick before. He ended up a clear winner, so we encouraged him to drain another bottle before reminding him that we were still waiting to hear his story.

"How about your stories?" he asked.

"Don't say you weren't listening? We've already told you all about ourselves and now it's your turn."

"Nothing much to tell really."

"Try starting from the beginning."

We listened, spellbound—full of admiration for the man's patience and single-minded determination to better himself. It had taken him ten years of careful planning before he could at last realise his dream to beat the system—and to do it so successfully that he could now travel anywhere he wanted at any time.

It didn't take long for his personality to take over. With one sweep of his hand, he cleared the table and picked up the little black case that he always carried with him. He plonked it down on the table and produced his passport, then he opened the case by releasing a special catch on the side. This revealed a small compartment, containing a special tray.

"You see," he commenced, "I realised before I started that, if my plan was to succeed, I would need to have, as it were, two passports—the one which you see here and, even more important, the one which I shall now produce.

"I should add that, when you open the case in the normal way, you will find documents which may look important, but which are of no importance in comparison to the treasure trove which I shall now show you—a treasure trove which enables me to travel the world with impunity."

He reached inside the case and produced a tray of

golden nuggets, which we soon realised constituted a magnificent collection of gold teeth. They nestled comfortably side by side, each in its own velvet-lined compartment. Each compartment contained a ticket, listing the weight, size and value of its contents. We gazed in wonder at his treasure trove. The top and sides of the tray contained details of its distinguished owner:- 'Dr Medicine Aram Kuryokhin, Dental Surgeon and President of the Armenian Dental Association of the Union of Soviet Socialist Republics.'

"You see," said Aram, "all this was an essential part of my original plan. You may know that Armenia lies in the eastern half of the Soviet Union. I qualified as a doctor there after the war and many of my patients were Asiatic Russians, who, as you may know, habitually display their wealth in a mouthful of gold teeth. You may also know that gold teeth are virtually indestructible. About ten years ago, I decided on my plan. I realised that I had got as far as I could as a doctor, so I switched to dentistry. I studied for several years before qualifying as a dental surgeon (and, incidentally, perfecting my English), by which time my ten-year plan was well under way. I became an enthusiastic member of the newly formed Armenian Dental Association and, in due course, was elected to their committee, after which it was only a matter of time before such an enthusiastic committee member was nominated as Chairman. This soon led inevitably to the honour of becoming their new President. It was therefore only a matter of time before I was able to obtain this passport, with permission to travel around Europe to lecture on the advantages of gold fillings, which invariably outlived their owners.

"I wrote several articles about this, which were widely published in Europe and even in America, although, because of the Cold War, even their own Dental Congress committee had to travel to Montreal for my lectures— and the rest you already know. I am constantly invited to dental congresses, with all expenses paid, and a grateful government encourages my enthusiasm by issuing me with a priority travel pass, which may I add, is even more effective than being a personal friend of Madame Greteskaya."

We opened the last bottle of vodka and drank his health—his whole plan was so simple that we could hardly believe that no one had thought of it before. There was one final question, however, which had to be asked before we let him off the hook.

"How about the Cadillac and the captain and all that nonsense about you being the beneficial owner?"

"I must confess I've been holding out on you. This is a rather high-risk sideline which I prefer not to talk about. There is, of course, no 'wealthy Russian living in Montreal who donates cars to beneficial owners'. The Soviet authorities value their car industry and forbid people like myself to import expensive foreign cars, so the captain suggested we became partners in crime We imported our first car three years ago, a lovely old Buick. I paid for it of course and the captain brought it across for me. It may seem strange to you, but our monolithic bureaucracy still allows captains of vessels over a certain tonnage to take their cars and their wives on ocean crossings—a throwback to the days when captains of barges habitually took their horses, bicycles and even their wives up and down the Volga as of right. This custom has never been repealed and, as is the way of things, it has now been enshrined in legal jargon so obscure that very few people even understand it, let alone query it."

"But why all this nonsense of beneficial owner?"

"Obvious, isn't it?—they couldn't possibly allow people like me to import valuable motor cars by bribing captains, so we hit on the idea of beneficial ownership, by which Russian citizens living abroad were allowed to send cars to their friends and relatives in the Soviet Union without upsetting our usual strict car quotas. This would obviously strengthen the overall economy, as beneficial owners would have to pay the usual import duty and the authorities here would take their own cut before handing the rest to the government, so everyone was happy. What else do you expect when everything is controlled so rigidly? People will always find a way round, and the result?—a dishonest and corrupt society."

Quite a speech, really. We finished the last bottle and were just settling down for the night when the police officer returned.

"You're all in luck," he said. "We've found the owners of the Volvo. We haven't questioned them yet, but we've taken their keys and had a look inside the car. Their documents seem to be in order, but the mystery remains as to how they were able to enter the dock area without an official pass. We've sent for a Swedish interpreter to question them and you are now free to go."

"What time is it now?" asked Wally.

The officer looked at his watch.

"Eighteen hundred. I should have left hours ago, but I've still got those wretched boys to interview."

Wally persevered.

"D'you think I can manage Tallinn tonight if I leave straightaway?"

The officer frowned.

"You know of course that they close the frontier at midnight—you'll have to get a move on if you want to get across before then—it may be worth a try, but the roads aren't all that good and most garages have run out of petrol by then. You'll be all right once you've crossed into Estonia—no road blocks there to hold you up."

Aram rose to his feet and towered over the officer.

"I might as well be on my way too—it's so dark in here that we thought it was quite late."

"There's a clock on the wall, sir, but it seems to have been damaged—perhaps one of the vodka glasses hit it by mistake."

"Quite so," said Aram, surveying the damage. He was impressed—the fellow had stood his ground, yet he still called him sir—he liked that.

"I'll be off then—it will take me a day or two, but I've got a good car and the main road to Georgia and Armenia was upgraded last year."

The police officer gave a half-smile and turned to me.

"And how is madam?"

"Madam, when she wakes up, will probably have a monumental hangover. I would be grateful if we could stay here for a while until she recovers."

"Of course, sir, I quite understand, but I hope you won't mind if we interview the Swedish boys in here when the interpreter arrives."

"Of course not, as long as we're not in the way."

Wally and Aram were ready to go now, so we went

42

outside to see them off. We shook hands all round and Aram gave me a little note for Joanna.

"Please tell your charming wife I shall always remember her and the happy hours we spent together on the *Pushkin*."

The swine—but a likeable swine for all that.

We watched them leave, Wally in a cloud of smoke and Aram, suave and confident in his magnificent Cadillac, purring gently and effortlessly as he overtook the Hillman on the straight. Two great characters, each as different as chalk from cheese, but each in their own way as Russian as they come.

As they left, an elegant-looking lady in a blue car drew up and introduced herself.

"Are these the two miscreants?"

"They are indeed, madam," said the police officer." Shall we all go inside and you can find out how on earth these two boys managed to drive from Sweden to Norway and a thousand miles up the Arctic highway from Trondheim to the Soviet frontier, then on to Leningrad, and, finally, without being challenged, into this prohibited dock area. If young people can do this sort of thing with impunity, what hope is there for law and order?"

"What hope indeed?"

"This is of course their story and it remains to be seen if it is correct. They actually speak quite good English although I'm sure you'll be able to question them more fully in their own language."

She looked at the youngsters—they were indeed ridiculously young for such an adventurous journey, no more than boys really—probably in their early twenties.

"Perhaps you frightened them and they decided it was best not to say anything."

"Perhaps I did, but it can't be helped. I couldn't care less how they managed to cross from Finland without entry visas, but I must find out how on earth they managed to enter the dock area without being stopped. We only have four entrances and these are guarded night and day. It is essential that they tell you which gate they used. Our whole security is under threat unless you can let us know exactly how they managed to get in without being challenged."

The interpreter quite understood, so I felt it was time to introduce myself.

"I feel I should mention that my wife is still inside. She's not feeling well, so I hope you won't mind if we stay for a while if we promise not to interrupt."

"Of course not."

The police officer led the way and I followed, with the interpreter close behind.

Joanna was sitting up, wild-eyed and distraught. She was trying desperately to concentrate and she gave a sigh of relief when she saw the interpreter.

"Ah—Madam Greteskaya—I've been waiting such a long time to meet you and now at last you've come to my rescue."

Three

The Hotel Lenin overlooked the Nevsky Prospekt. It was a massive structure with enormous glass windows, which, had the glass been of better quality, would have afforded the fortunate guests an unrivalled view of the beautiful city beneath them.

We finally arrived and I parked Yoddy outside the main entrance, then I heaved Joanna and one suitcase up the steps and through the massive front door. The lobby was jam-packed with guests, some queuing at the solitary desk and others wandering around aimlessly. The scene reminded me somehow of a huge cathedral, with worshippers waiting for Communion, while others—less motivated perhaps—gawked at the stained glass windows and pretended to be interested in the architecture.

"All I want to do," mumbled Joanna, "is go straight to bed—and the sooner the better."

"So you shall."

I looked around in despair. We'd have to jump the queue somehow—but how? I suddenly saw a half-open door in a corner of the lobby. I can't think why, but it reminded me in some way of a door leading to the vestry—not that I'm much of an authority on churches, but it was worth a try.

"Wait here," I said, with as much authority as I could muster. "Keep an eye on your case and I'll see what I can do."

I fought my way through the crowd and pushed open the door.

An elderly lady looked up from her desk, irritated at the interruption.

"You can't come in here," she said in German, "this is the manager's office."

Thank goodness she spoke German. She was obviously used to German tourists barging their way in—no Russian would have dared enter her sanctuary without an appointment.

"Artzt," I shouted, and, for good measure, "meine Frau ist schwer Krank."

Action at last.

She pressed a red button on her desk and a loud,

bleeping noise echoed through the cathedral. Everyone stopped talking and waited for something to happen. It could be a fire or even a cardiac arrest. Joanna, tired of waiting, was now lying down in the middle of the lobby and I knew that I had to get to her first before professional help arrived, so I ran towards her and shook her awake.

"You're ill," I hissed in her ear, "you may have had a cardiac arrest."

Confronted with such alarming news, she tried to get to her feet.

"No, keep lying down—pretend to be asleep."

"But I was asleep until you woke me up."

"Listen carefully, this is different—the idea now is how to jump the queue without being found out. Help is on its way—all you have to do is go to sleep again."

Joanna, bless her, got the message straightaway and collapsed on the floor. First to arrive were two hospital porters with a trolley, but they were prevented from lifting her by several onlookers insisting that she be given the last rites first. The priest was apparently on his way and, while we were waiting, I decided to make good use of the trolley by asking them to help me fetch the rest of the luggage from Yoddy. By the time we returned, the cavalry had arrived in the shape of a tall, priestly figure, who was sprinkling holy water over the recumbent figure and about to give it his final blessing. Assisting him was an ominous Rasputin look-alike and I knew then that it was high time to intervene.

Joanna rose to the occasion straightaway. Her eyelids flickered and she groaned convincingly.

"Where am I?" she asked.

Even I hadn't fully realised her undoubted talent as

an actress. She was now in the limelight and thoroughly enjoying the experience. She was the centre of attention, she was in charge and everyone would do her bidding.

"I want to go to bed now," she said, calmly and deliberately.

"And so you shall."

A young doctor had arrived and was kneeling down beside her. He waved aside the priestly figures and examined her carefully, whereupon she rolled towards him with every sign of enthusiasm.

"I don't feel very well," she said, smiling seductively.

"Of course you don't," he said, keeping his distance. "You've had a nasty turn, but I don't think it's all that serious. I'll just check your pulse and your blood pressure and then we'll take you straight up to your room."

The porters and the trolley were standing by and there was a ripple of applause as the leading players made their exit. Joanna, sitting on the trolley amid the luggage, smiled and blew kisses towards those who had come to her rescue in her hour of need and they waved back. Even the priest and his assistant waved, although with a noticeable lack of enthusiasm.

A nurse was waiting for us upstairs and she helped Joanna undress and get into bed.

"All she needs is a good night's sleep—she'll be right as rain in the morning."

I suddenly remembered Yoddy, still parked outside on double yellow lines.

"Don't worry," said the doctor, "They'd never dare book anyone staying here."

Reassured, I unpacked the suitcases, made sure that Joanna was sleeping peacefully and took the lift downstairs.

It had a disconcerting habit of stopping at each floor, with doors opening and closing automatically, although, apart from this slight eccentricity and a few squeaks and groans, it seemed safe enough.

I drove Yoddy round to the car park at the back of the hotel and locked the doors, then I strolled back and climbed the steps to the main entrance. I was about to go inside when I noticed a forlorn-looking, middle-aged man sitting on the wall His left arm was in a sling and he looked so dejected that I stopped and spoke to him.

"I've had a perfectly dreadful day," he said in German. "In fact, a perfectly dreadful three days."

He looked as though he might burst into tears at any moment.

"I haven't got any money either."

Fancy a German, of all people, short of money—sufficiently intriguing to dispel any misgivings that he might be a confidence trickster. Perhaps he had lost his wallet?

"No—much worse than that."

Having jumped the queue and parked the car safely, I was in a generous mood.

"Tell you what," I said, "come inside and I'll buy you a drink, then you can tell me your story."

"Thank you so much," he said. "I'm so grateful."

Another phenomenon, a grateful German—even more intriguing.

We went down to the bar and I noticed that he made a beeline for the peanuts and crisps. Perhaps he hadn't eaten all day.

"You'll never believe what happened to me," he began. "Try me."

By this time I was ready to go along with almost anything, however ridiculous. Whatever else lay in store for us, our stay at the Hotel Lenin was unlikely to be boring.

"You really will never believe this—but perhaps I should start at the beginning."

"Good idea," I said, and bought him another drink.

He was a technical engineer, employed by a large manufacturer of colour printers.

"The Soviet authorities," he said, "invited us to participate in an exhibition which is being held in Moscow this week as part of their latest five-year plan. We had a few teething problems with our latest colour printer. It should have been delivered last week, but, to speed things up a bit, we decided to ship it to Leningrad and then by low loader to Moscow, so I was sent to Leningrad to supervise the unloading."

So far, so good.

"You'll never guess what comes next. I arrived three days ago and booked into the Lenin for the night, then I went straight down to the docks to check that the low loader had arrived to take the printer to Moscow. I rang our office in Moscow and told them when to expect it, then I waited for the ship to arrive."

The recollection of what happened next upset him to such an extent that I rapidly bought him another drink.

"You're not going to believe this," he said finally. "The crane driver must have been drunk or something. Our crate came straight towards the low loader, missing it by inches, and crashed to the ground a few feet away—he must have dropped it well before it landed, as the crate exploded and I got a nasty splinter in my left hand, the fleshy part between thumb and forefinger. I pulled it out and my hand bled like a pig, but worse things have happened in my time, so I wrapped my handkerchief around it and waited while we inspected the damage. Our people had packed it well and the printer itself wasn't damaged, so we got another crane to lift it up on the low loader and I saw the driver off to Moscow before taking a taxi back to the hotel. I'd had a long day and I felt a bit groggy, so I had a glass or two of vodka and went straight to bed. I woke up feeling terrible and, as soon as I saw how badly my hand was swollen, I remembered that I hadn't had an anti-tetanus injection for ages, so I panicked and pressed the emergency button beside the phone.

"Someone came straightaway and before I realised what was happening, two men in white coats carried me off on a stretcher and took me to hospital."

I couldn't help feeling glad that Joanna hadn't ended up in hospital—that would have been a disaster.

"They gave me a tetanus injection, then they took all my clothes to be fumigated—the cheek of it—then they gave me a typhoid injection. 'Why typhoid?' I asked, but they just smiled and went on giving me injections until my arm was like a pin cushion, then they put me in a hot bath full of revolting disinfectant and I had to stay in hospital for two whole days. I couldn't leave without my clothes of course and it wasn't until this morning that they finally discharged me. I still had my key, so I went straight up to my room, only to find someone else there. As if that wasn't enough, my luggage had disappeared and I had to queue for ages before I managed to find someone who knew what had happened—and do you know what she said?"

Nothing would surprise me by now.

"She said my room was only booked for one night and, as it was needed for someone else, they packed my things and forwarded them to the Moscow address I'd given when I arrived. I asked her what she intended to do about it and—you'll never believe this—she shrugged her shoulders and turned away. I was so mad I could have hit her."

The very thought brought tears to his eyes, so I hastily bought what I hoped would be his last drink.

"I've been wandering around all day, trying to phone or telex Moscow, but nothing works properly in this wretched place. Moscow must have been trying to get in touch with me too, but nothing's come through and no one here seems to care what happens to me. I left my passport and credit cards in my room when I went down to the docks and they sent absolutely everything off to Moscow, so what I have in my pockets is all I have in the world—hardly any cash and barely enough for a train ticket, so I'm off to Moscow on the first train tomorrow morning."

He finished his drink and we shook hands.

"Goodbye, old chap—I do hope you'll find somewhere to sleep."

I gave him some loose change and it was then he started to cry. Embarrassed, I looked away, then he suddenly smiled and I knew he'd be all right.

"Give me your card," he said. "I'll let you know how many colour printers we've sold."

Four

Joanna was still asleep when I returned. The nurse had tucked her in, but I hadn't realised she had nothing on. The room was warm and she'd thrown back the blankets. She was so beautiful that I just stood there, gazing at her, remembering how lucky I was. Moonlight streamed through the window and she half-opened her eyes. Her lips were moist and a smile hovered there—dreaming perhaps of the young doctor who had come to her rescue a few hours earlier. I bent down and kissed her and fondled her breasts, ever so gently. She smiled and opened her eyes:

"So it's you," she said.

"Were you dreaming about me?"

"Not sure really, but seeing you're here…"

"Now for some breakfast."

"Good idea—I'm starving."

The hotel guide assured us that there was a dining room on every floor, so we followed the 'Zaptrak' sign, which Joanna assured me was Russian for breakfast. The corridor seemed endless, but we eventually came to a large potted plant guarded by an elderly crone. She greeted us cordially and pointed a bony finger in the right direction, so we carried on.

The sun shone through the huge glass windows which lined the corridor—windows which, albeit opaque, transmitted an eerie light; the combination of the never-ending corridor, the bright sun shining through the distorted glass and the elderly crone reminded us somehow of Alice in Wonderland

"All we need now," said Joanna, "is a magic password—how about Zaptrak?"

"Good idea."

We pressed on and, joy of joys, the Zaptrak room at last. Real people, sitting down and eating breakfast. They'd even managed to open one of the windows and there, before our very eyes, stretched the full length of the glorious Nevsky Prospect.

A waitress brought us coffee, fresh rolls, salami, jam and real English marmalade—so much for Aram's gloomy predictions of gastronomic disaster. I thought of the German engineer—he could have done with a good breakfast.

There were four German tourists at the next table, drinking champagne, so I asked them if they'd seen anything of the unfortunate German technician who'd been incarcerated in hospital for three days and had lost all his luggage.

"What sort of technician?" they asked.

"Printing machines," I explained. "Huge, four-colour printers—the largest manufacturer in Germany."

"Ah, that would be Heidelberg in West Germany—very good they are, too."

"Then you're from East Germany?"

"Of course—you won't find many West Germans here."

I realised then why so many Russians spoke German—

they were used to tourists from the DDR and automatically assumed that we too were German.

We waved our Zaptrak coupons as we left, but no one seemed to want them.

"Never mind," said Joanna, "they'll come in handy for lunch, or even afternoon tea."

The thought of sitting down to a dainty tea in Leningrad and paying for it with a breakfast coupon added to our enjoyment and we were delighted when the dear old lady guarding the potted plant—crone no longer—gave a toothless grin and insisted on shaking hands when we passed her again on our way out.

"Perhaps she makes the cucumber sandwiches for tea."

Joanna's laugh was infectious and we were still laughing when we reached our room.

"I feel like another lie down now," she sighed. "Perhaps you'd like to go downstairs and see if you can buy some petrol coupons, then, while you're there, try to buy some tickets for the ballet this evening—and make sure you get the best seats, nothing less will do for our very first visit to the Kirov."

"Hope you enjoy your rest," I muttered, with more than a hint of sarcasm.

"I'll have a bath and I'll be waiting for you when you come back."

One never knows with Joanna—full of Eastern promise one moment and hard to get the next—but never mind, last night was great.

The donkey plodded along the corridor towards the ancient lift—stick ever present, but anticipation of succulent carrot ever before him. It might even be the element of uncertainty which would improve the flavour.

How boring life would be, he thought, if one always knew exactly what was in store.

Joanna, for instance—outwardly shy, but an emotional tiger when roused. The tiger was great for making love, but had certain disadvantages—her total unpredictability, for instance—although, to be fair, she never tried to hide anything and her occasional flirtations were an open secret. Above all, she was fun to live with and has always been my lifelong friend and comrade. She was a wonderful mother to our three boys and they absolutely adored her. She was a great home lover and even after John Richards had told us about his visits to the Soviet Union, she was still reluctant to leave home, but, in the end, her love of ballet was so overwhelming that she was quite unable to resist the temptation of the two most succulent carrots of all, the Kirov and the Bolshoi.

The usual queues were waiting in the lobby, so I decided to check Yoddy's tank before buying petrol coupons. She was still where I'd left her, surrounded by a dozen or so Skodas and Trabants with DDR number plates, but there was a slight problem. The gates of the car park were shut tight and padlocked, even though the brochure stated quite clearly that the hotel car park was open twenty-four hours a day.

There was no point in buying petrol coupons as long as Yoddy was imprisoned in the car park, so I joined the queue in the lobby and, after half an hour, finally arrived at the reception desk, only to be confronted by a receptionist who couldn't care less. She was pretending to look for something—the usual excuse for ignoring everyone—and I waited patiently until she deigned to acknowledge my presence.

"Yes?" she asked, without looking up.

I managed a smile and began to tell her about the locked car park, whereupon, without saying a word, she reached under the desk and produced a brochure. She unfolded it and underlined something before handing it to me and it was only then that I realised it was the same brochure as the one we already had.

It was already too late. In that split second, she had turned to the person behind me and I had no choice but to return to the back of the queue and start all over again. I decided then and there that nothing less than a serious confrontation would suffice. If this didn't do the trick, I would report her to the manager for insolence. I would give her one last chance and, if she ignored me again, I would make a scene.

My resolve strengthened as I drew nearer the front of the queue.

I wouldn't even give her time to think. She'd had her chance and she hadn't even bothered to listen to what I was saying. She didn't look up and she didn't even speak to me or acknowledge my presence.

So be it—I would thump the desk and demand to see the manager. I would suggest to him that receptionists were there to try to help people, not ignore them, and, as she was apparently incapable of being even reasonably polite, the sooner he got rid of her the better.

I finally reached the head of the queue. I opened the brochure she had given me and banged it down in front of her, then I thumped the desk as hard as I could.

There was a sudden hush and she looked up at last before retreating in horror. No one had ever made a fuss like this before. She realised that everyone was staring at her, waiting to see what she'd do next. She looked around helplessly like a startled rabbit. What on earth was she supposed to do? Perhaps the man was a lunatic—he might even have a knife.

She started to cry, but no one came to help her, so she abandoned her desk and rushed across the lobby to the manager's office. She opened the door without even knocking and disappeared inside, slamming the door behind her.

There was a murmur of anticipation. Someone had made a scene. He could only be a foreigner of some sort, perhaps even a commissar from Moscow—no ordinary Soviet citizen who valued his freedom would dare thump the desk in an Intourist hotel.

The door opened and the manager appeared. He was a small, affable little man and he smiled at the assembled multitude. He gave the impression that, whatever the problem and however obscure the language, he was more than capable of dealing with it. He looked around and cleared his throat.

"What seems to be the trouble?"

He repeated the question in several languages and, when there was no reply, he walked slowly towards me.

"What seems to be the problem?" he asked, smiling cautiously.

"Your receptionist is the problem," I said. "She ignores everyone—no wonder you have such large queues."

"She is already in my office and has apologised to me for her bad behaviour," he announced pontifically. "I myself will be only too pleased to deal personally with any problem you may have."

There was a gasp. The new manager had actually offered

to help someone who had made a fuss—things must be improving at last.

He came closer, smiling effusively, trying to decide whether I was foreign, important or quite mad. As far as he was concerned these were the three most likely categories of troublemakers rash enough to make scenes in officially credited Intourist hotels.

"I'm sorry to trouble you," I explained, "but the car park's locked and I can't get to my car."

The condescending smile vanished and his whole attitude changed immediately.

"It is we who should apologise to you," he replied in perfect English. "Would you be kind enough to come to my office?"

Once there, he led the way to an alcove, with a coffee table and two easy chairs.

"Please make yourself comfortable. I'm Boris Ostrovsky, the new manager. I'll do my best to explain about the car park, but, before we start, how about a nice cup of English tea?"

He crossed the room and spoke to his secretary. She ushered the distraught girl out of the room and returned shortly with a kettle and a teapot, while the manager sat down beside me and produced a leaflet in Russian and German.

"This leaflet may explain why our car park is locked— copies should have been inserted in each brochure, but they have only just arrived. Other languages are less important at present."

"Why are they less important?"

He poured the tea before he replied.

"It's a matter of priorities—most guests who bring their

own cars are either Russian, Polish or East German, so these are the guests more likely to need the leaflets. I should explain now that Leningrad has been chosen to pioneer an important experiment to encourage car owners to leave their cars at home and use public transport instead."

"You may well ask why we and not Moscow have been chosen for this honour. The official reason is that car ownership in Moscow is now so widespread that it's far too late to embark on such an experiment, although the real reason is almost certainly that our lords and masters in Moscow are reluctant to surrender their luxurious limousines."

"Our lovely city of Leningrad therefore has the honour of blazing the Soviet ecological trail. We have already reduced the cost of bus travel to a level where the expense of collecting fares is almost more than the cost of running the bus, so we plan to abolish fares altogether next year."

I was impressed.

"But why does all this concern us?"

"I was coming to that—guests who come here are, in Soviet terms, privileged people. Many have their own cars and it's obviously unfair for them to be seen driving around, using up petrol and polluting the atmosphere, when they can travel around more easily and certainly much more cheaply by public transport."

"The three largest hotels in Leningrad, of which we are one, have therefore agreed to participate in an experiment whereby, for a short while, their car parks become bonded warehouses, where guests can leave their cars for safekeeping until they depart. I need hardly add that a free bus service to anywhere in Leningrad is provided in exchange."

"That reminds me," I said. "I hope you won't mind my changing the subject, but my wife and I were hoping to go to the Kirov tonight and I was about to buy tickets when you were kind enough to intervene in another matter and I lost my place in the queue."

"Of course—I'll be glad to help you—how many tickets would you like?"

"Just two will be fine."

"No, I mean how many nights?—there's a different ballet each night."

"Four nights would be wonderful."

He opened a drawer and produced eight tickets.

"There—these will help compensate for our dreadful queuing problems."

"Thank you so much—how much do I owe you?"

"Please have these on the house in recognition of your kindness in agreeing to leave your car in our bonded warehouse."

We were getting on like a house on fire and I decided to ask him a final favour.

"My wife has reminded me that we have to buy enough petrol coupons to take us to Moscow next week."

"Ah—I'm afraid I can't help you with this one. The fuel commissariat keeps a tight control on all fuel, so you have to go to their office in the lobby to purchase your daily ration, although, with your car in the pound, you'll have twice as much as you need for the journey to Moscow."

How kind these people were when you got to know them—and how unpredictable. We'd only been in

Leningrad for two days, but we'd already experienced enough to last for a week or more, locked up as soon as we arrived, jumping the queue in the hotel lobby, getting past the dear old crone guarding the potted plant, devouring a free breakfast, meeting friendly East Germans and helping to rescue a West German from disaster, laughing our heads off at the thought of the old crone making dainty cucumber sandwiches for afternoon tea, confronting a surly receptionist and meeting her friendly new manager, who actually apologised for her behaviour and gave us free tickets for the Kirov ballet—and of course, the completely unexpected—poor Yoddy, locked in the hotel car park, impounded without warning.

The whole thing seemed so unreal that I started to laugh and he insisted on hearing everything that had happened.

"Tell me again why they locked you up as soon as you arrived—it's almost unbelievable."

I related the saga of our brief imprisonment for importing a car without a licence and he laughed at the absurdity of it all, so I told him all about Wally and Aram, our fellow prisoners, and the two Swedish boys who had outwitted the might of the Soviet Union.

"Serve you all right for coming to the Soviet Union in the first place."

I thanked him again for his help and joined the petrol queue in the lobby. This didn't take long and the returning hero, donkey no longer, marched triumphantly back to his room.

His carrot, his reward for having surmounted the perils of the Hotel Lenin, was lying on the bed.

"What kept you?" she asked.

The next few days were simply wonderful. I remember catching the hotel minibus as far as the Kirov Bridge, then walking across the River Neva towards the Hermitage Museum. Halfway across, Joanna stopped and there were tears in her eyes.

"What a beautiful city this is," she said. "I'm sure there's a special name for it."

I tried hard to remember—if only I could—then it suddenly came to me.

"I know—they call it the Venice of the north."

"Fancy remembering that—how clever you are."

She leaned over and gave me a kiss.

"I'm so happy here!" she exclaimed suddenly. "Thank you for bringing me, I've always wanted to come to Russia, ever since I was a little girl, and now I'm actually here, in beautiful Leningrad, and we're going to the ballet tonight."

She looked across at the Hermitage, dominating the far bank.

"That's where we must go tomorrow."

"Good idea." I was happy to agree. "It will probably take all day and even then you'll only have seen the half of it, so perhaps we should plan to go twice."

She gazed at a massive equestrian statue dominating the skyline and we walked towards it.

"That's Peter the Great," I said. "He founded Leningrad in 1703."

We referred to the guide book.

This huge statue—we read—is known as the Bronze Horseman (after Pushkin's poem of the same name) and is one of the finest achievements of monumental sculpture in the Soviet Union. It was created in 1782 by Etienne-Maurice Falconet and the pedestal is carved from a single piece of granite rock. The statue is eight metres high and weighs sixteen hundred tons, et cetera, et cetera.

We crossed the bridge and wandered along the far bank, looking at the barges and pleasure boats and—unexpectedly—the hydrofoils, which, balanced precariously on huge rudders, lifted themselves out of the water as they gathered speed.

We found a tea place overlooking the river—nothing much by western standards, but the samovar gave the tea a special taste, adding somehow to the pleasure of the day.

We didn't walk far, only far enough to confirm our first impressions of the beautiful city around us, then we caught a bus back to our hotel.

The special coach which was to take us to the ballet arrived at 1900 and we were interested to see it was a West German Mercedes—evidence that the Soviet authorities were quite willing to trade with West Germany if it suited them. We climbed aboard and found ourselves sitting next to a middle-aged couple. They were speaking in English, so we introduced ourselves and they greeted us cordially.

"I'm Lars and this is my partner Ingrid. I don't expect we'll leave for another ten minutes or so, but don't worry—the ballet doesn't start till eight o'clock."

I couldn't help commenting on the luxury coach and they told us that there were quite a few West German Mercedes coaches in Leningrad.

"Our coach is shared between three hotels, the Baltiiskaya, the Europa and yours. The driver will take us to the Kirov and bring us back again afterwards—all part of the service."

"Which is your hotel?" I asked.

"The Europa, overlooking the Neva—luxurious and very expensive."

"For capitalists only, I assume."

They smiled and looked at each other.

"Most certainly, although, in our case, it's one of the perks of the job. I should perhaps explain that Ingrid and I are both architects. Our company specialises in hotel design and we were fortunate enough to be asked to upgrade the Europa three years ago, which we managed to do quite successfully. We're under contract to follow up from time to time to sort out any problems which arise—all expenses paid of course. Incidentally, you may be interested to hear we've got some decent glass in the windows at last, which is more than you have."

How on earth did he know that?

"The Russians had difficulty in producing large sheets of glass without blemishes, so we put them on to your people in England—Pilkingtons, I think they were—and they came up with the solution. I supervised the installation myself and all is well, so I'm Leningrad's blue-eyed boy at the moment."

"Do you design other hotels?"

"Yes, Ingrid and I were in New York last month and—I'll tell you one thing—we feel much safer here in Leningrad than we did in downtown New York. Ingrid had her handbag snatched in broad daylight and we were nearly mugged one evening after dark, whereas here in

Leningrad, even after midnight, we feel perfectly safe when we're walking back from the theatre to our hotel."

The stragglers arrived and the guide checked numbers, then the coach purred into life and a carefully modulated voice came over the intercom.

'We shall arrive at the theatre at approximately seven-thirty and the performance will commence at eight. Please be in your seats by seven forty-five."

"All very efficient," I whispered.

"Don't miss the intervals," said our new friend. "Up the stairs—with real caviar and free champagne; make sure you don't lose out."

His English was so good that it took me a while to realise that, with names like Lars and Ingrid, they were obviously Swedish.

The coach stopped outside the Kirov and we alighted into a beautiful autumn evening. The sun was setting and spotlights illuminated the facade, giving it a strange, other-worldly radiance. We filed into the huge auditorium, which, with its sky-blue seats and celestial golden curtains, filled us with wonder and awe. We were on the threshold of a heavenly new world we had never even imagined—a Russian Paradise.

Tchaikovsky's thrilling overture to *The Sleeping Beauty* plunged us into a heaven of dreams and imagination. The first interval came as a shock, an unwanted intrusion. The golden curtain fell, but Joanna was still dreaming, so I went upstairs with Lars and Ingrid to find flunkeys in Czarist uniforms handing out free glasses of champagne and real caviar sandwiches, one of which I managed to smuggle downstairs for Joanna.

"Lots more sandwiches upstairs," I said encouragingly.

"Champagne as well, so why don't you come with us for the second interval?"

Even worlds of dreams and imagination can't last forever, but it must have been midnight before the last curtain fell amid tumultuous applause. Our coach was waiting outside and Lars and Ingrid got out at the luxurious Hotel Europa. Our next stop was the Baltiiskaya and finally the Lenin, where I shepherded a tired and happy Joanna upstairs—thank goodness the lift was still working.

Lars and Ingrid had offered to show us round the Hermitage the next day.

"You'd never believe," he'd said during the first interval, "how many treasures they have stored away in the basement where no one ever sees them—even the staff don't know what's there, so I don't suppose anyone else does either. The catalogue doesn't even list them and I've been trying for ages to get permission to visit their underground maze. The rooms are air-conditioned too and I nearly managed to get a permit a few years ago when we were installing air-conditioning in the Europa. I told them I wanted to find out whether Soviet air-conditioning plants were up to scratch before we started, but I got a flea in my ear from Moscow, so that was that."

It was then that I'd invited them to breakfast.

"Good idea," he said. "What time would you like us to arrive?"

"How about ten o'clock?"

"Fine—that means we'll be making an early start, with plenty of time for the Hermitage afterwards—where would you like to meet us?"

"No use going to the reception—you'll be queuing all day if you do. Just take the lift to the third floor and walk half a mile until you come to an old crone hiding behind a potted plant at the end of the corridor. The walk will help you work up an appetite and, as a bonus, you'll also have an unique opportunity of inspecting our opaque pre-Pilkington windows. We'll wait for you in the dining room, just past the old crone."

"How about breakfast coupons?"

"No one seems to bother much about them—we still haven't used the ones they sold us on the *Pushkin*."

Joanna was still asleep the next morning and I was about to congratulate myself on my undoubted ability to plan ahead when I remembered that I hadn't even told her. The excuse that she was asleep by the time we got back from the Kirov, however true, certainly wouldn't wash, so I woke her gently with a cup of tea before asking her, quite casually, if she would like to spend the day at the Hermitage.

Certainly she would —very much indeed.

"You remember the Swedish couple we met last night?"

"Those nice people?—of course I do."

"They've offered to show us round—they might even join us for breakfast."

She looked at me suspiciously.

"Did you invite them to breakfast or not?"

"Lars was going to come anyway—he wanted to have a look at our crazy windows, he really couldn't believe they were that bad."

"Are they coming to breakfast or not?"

"Yes—almost certainly—they'll be here about ten."

"What time is it now?"

"Half past eight."

They were already there when we arrived.

"Thanks for the directions," said Lars, "but we could have done without the lift."

"Why?—didn't it work?"

"Yes, it worked fine—stopped in all the right places, including an unscheduled stop that frightened the life out of us."

"You shouldn't have worried," I said. "It does that from time to time. All you have to do is wait for a minute or two until it starts again—don't forget that it's the element of uncertainty which lends life its flavour. Where's your sense of adventure?"

"Certainly not on the third floor of the Lenin. I know a bit about lifts and this business of stopping on each floor is fraught with hazard. The solenoid wears out eventually and, if the lift isn't serviced regularly—and I'm sorry to say that this one hasn't been serviced for ages— anyone inside is well and truly up the creek, either stranded for hours or, even worse, flat as a pancake at the bottom of the lift shaft."

I made a mental note to ask the manager when the lift had last been serviced.

We looked around for a table and were fortunate enough to find one by an open window.

"What a glorious view!" exclaimed Ingrid. "Even better than the Europa."

They were even more impressed when breakfast arrived.

"I don't believe it," she said. "Real English marmalade— now who are the capitalists?"

"Ingrid and I have a suggestion," said Lars. "As you know, this evening's concert starts earlier than usual."

We nodded convincingly—we didn't know, but perhaps we should have.

"It's more of—shall we say—a social evening to enable pupils and young students of the Kirov Ballet School to do their stuff. It starts at six and finishes about eight and we might be able to meet some of the dancers and even one or two of the principals afterwards. The students who have graduated will go up to the restaurant upstairs to receive their awards—that's the room where we had our champagne and caviar last night, though all we'll probably get is a cup of coffee—then, if you're feeling up to it, we'd like to invite you to our hotel for dinner afterwards."

I glanced at Joanna. She looked really pleased and I knew how much she'd been looking forward to an evening like this ever since we left England. As for me, the invitation to dinner provided a useful, additional incentive.

"What a splendid idea—thank you so much."

Joanna decided she'd like to go back to our room first, so we arranged to meet downstairs in half an hour or so.

"Of course, but, if you don't mind, we would rather go down in this lift—it looks a bit safer than the other one."

"Which lift?"

"That one over there, where it says 'lift'."

Sure enough, almost hidden by another potted plant, was a modern lift with sliding doors. They opened and closed smoothly without any of the squeaking and shuddering which we had assumed was part and parcel of life on the third floor of the Lenin.

"That's what I call a lift," said Lars. "German built and

properly serviced—no wonder no one uses the other one unless they have to."

"How did you know it was here?"

"I knew there would have to be another one this end—have you ever known a hotel this size without at least two lifts? You may decide to use this one so as not to keep us waiting while you're stuck. By the way, where would you like us to meet?"

"The lobby's always crowded, so the steps outside would probably be safer—see you in half an hour then."

They were waiting for us outside and we caught a bus straightaway. It all seemed so easy and I realised then how pleasant life would be if public transport was as reliable and inexpensive as it was in Leningrad.

I said as much to Lars.

"We have something like this in Stockholm," he said, "but it's more expensive and, without restrictions on cars and lorries, many of the advantages are lost."

We walked across the square and into the courtyard of the Hermitage.

We stood for a while, gazing upwards, admiring the magnificent building which had been restored so lovingly since the war. We hesitated on the threshold as one might when entering some magnificent cathedral, then we pushed open the huge entrance door and hesitated again while we took in the grandeur of the interior. We stood there quietly—not speaking, scarcely moving.

The anteroom contained original paintings and posters depicting the heroic struggles of the 1922 revolution and we noticed two elderly ladies, one on each side of the main entrance. They wore the type of headscarf we'd already seen in the Soviet Union and even the old lady behind the potted plant in the Lenin wore something similar. Lars explained that grandmothers, or 'babushki' as they were called, occupied an important place in Soviet society. They cared for babies and their own grandchildren, they swept up the autumn leaves and kept the streets clean, they cleaned the lavatories and public buildings and generally kept an eye open for potential troublemakers. They also guarded museums and art galleries, where their role, theoretically, was to offer assistance, although Lars insisted that, from a public order point of view, they were indispensable. I still wondered however if, at their age, they were of any real use as a deterrent.

"Don't let their age fool you," he said. "I was here once when some yob spat out his chewing gum and stamped on it. One of them was up like a shot and had him in an arm lock before you could say Jack Robinson. He was taller and heavier than she was, but she had him on the floor in no time and made him scrape up the gum with his fingernails before handing him over to a security guard."

"How about if something serious happened—shouting and fighting for instance?"

"I'm sure they'd be up to it—they're hand picked and I wouldn't be surprised if they're given special courses in unarmed combat."

The very thought of two elderly ladies wading into a pitched battle with arms flailing seemed unlikely until I noticed that, although apparently asleep, they were actually watching us intently under their all-enveloping headscarves. It was obvious that we too were suspicious characters—as foreigners, we might even be professional art thieves.

In a strange way, the very thought of being watched

made us feel uneasy and, to make matters worse, the knowledge that they were watching us made us feel so guilty that we soon moved on to the next room to avoid their gaze.

The next two exhibition rooms were a riot of colour, with eighteenth- and nineteenth-century Russian and European paintings well represented. Lars told us that, during the long and dreadful siege of Leningrad, when so many buildings were destroyed, the Hermitage had still managed to store and preserve most of their paintings, although a lot of them had been damaged and were still in the vaults, awaiting examination and professional opinion on the likelihood of successful restoration.

One of the rooms contained rare and valuable triptych paintings which had been donated to the Hermitage for safe-keeping after the revolution, when so many churches were neglected or destroyed. This room was closely guarded by four young-looking grandmothers, alert and ready for action. They looked so ferocious that I commented on their appearance.

"These young grandmothers are feared throughout the Soviet Union," explained Lars. "They flourish in the police force and the security services and they carry guns, which they don't hesitate to use when necessary."

"I suppose that's why they're so much younger than our old lady in the hotel."

"Of course—all she has to guard is her potted plant, whereas these beauties are responsible for these unique ikon and triptych paintings, worth several million roubles."

The museum opened out on to a courtyard and we decided to go outside for some fresh air, where we found a small lake with a fountain in the middle—one of the many beautiful fountains for which Leningrad is famous. We strolled around the lake to the other side, where, to our surprise, we found a little restaurant, tucked away under some trees. It looked so inviting that we decided we'd had enough culture for one day—it was time to abandon the Hermitage and concentrate on lunch.

"Privately owned restaurants are like gold dust in Leningrad," said Ingrid. "I knew this one was here, but Lars wouldn't listen to me. Isn't that typical of a man? They think they know everything, but they often overlook important things—and, believe you me, a privately owned restaurant in Leningrad is really something. I'm tired of eating in our hotel—the food is usually tasteless and the service abysmal."

Lars, the perfect diplomat, ordered French champagne and we enjoyed a splendid meal, all the better for being in the open air. We sat in the sunshine and relaxed long enough to ensure that it was much too late to return to the Hermitage even if we wanted to. Lars summed it up beautifully.

"Perhaps we should take advantage of the lovely weather and walk to the Kirov along the river bank—it's not all that far away and it won't matter if we're early. It's a beautiful theatre and we can always have a look around while we're waiting—did you know, by the way, that it seats nearly two thousand people?"

We arrived with an hour to spare and bought a programme with full details of the students who were to give their first public performance. It had a large photograph of Madame Greteskaya on the cover and, even though we knew she'd been banished to Moscow, Joanna became quite excited.

"Perhaps she'll be here tonight—perhaps the authorities will let her come after all, but even if they don't, we can find out where she lives in Moscow and go and see her when we get there."

The lights dimmed, the overture began and we were transported to Italy for *Romeo and Juliet*. The *corps de ballet* danced beautifully amid continuous applause and numerous encores. It didn't seem to matter that the scene shifters were busy preparing for the dress rehearsal of *Petrushka* which had been scheduled for early the following morning—all eyes were on the dancers

The performance ended, the lights went up and friends, families and hotel guests were invited upstairs to witness the presentation of awards to those students who had graduated from Leningrad's prestigious ballet school.

More applause, followed by an undignified scramble up the stairs. Joanna, waving her precious letter of introduction, was soon surrounded by an admiring crowd of beautiful boys and girls. They could hardly wait to hear what Madame had to say and Joanna was ecstatic. I felt so happy for her—her wish was starting to come true at last. I also enjoyed being lionised. Everyone wanted to know how we'd managed to drive all the way from England to Leningrad, just to meet them. The crush was so great that we found it difficult to understand what they were all saying, but one thing was clear, they absolutely worshipped Madame Greteskaya and they all missed her terribly.

Champagne arrived and the awards were presented. The acting principal gave a short speech, then we all drank a toast to Madame Greteskaya, their joy and inspiration for so many years, the best friend they ever had.

The festivities continued for another hour until it was time to for us to leave, but the students wouldn't let us go. They followed us down, still full of questions and requests: "When will you go to Moscow?—When will you see her?—Please give her our love and don't forget to buy her some flowers—here's twenty roubles in case you don't have the right money—She may be living at the Hotel Russia, near the Kremlin—We've all signed this programme, so please give it to her."

Joanna, flushed with pleasure and excitement, hugged and kissed them all, then they cheered us on our way. I found it difficult to imagine them getting up the following morning and presenting themselves at the crack of dawn for a gruelling dress rehearsal for a gala performance the same evening.

Even Lars and Ingrid were impressed.

"What fun they are—and how disciplined, but that's where they have the edge—discipline is an essential component of Russian ballet and has been for over a hundred years."

The foyer of the Hotel Europa was an eye opener—a long, curved counter, flanked by the very latest Beryosca shop on one side and a post office and telephone exchange on the other. The post office had public telephones, telex machines and copying facilities for the use of their guests, but the Beryosca shop was every Russian's dream.

"Herr Lindstrom?—telex for you from Stockholm, arrived this afternoon."

The receptionist, an attractive girl, remembered who

76

he was and, as we pushed through the swing doors, she came across the foyer to greet us.

She spoke to him in Swedish and greeted us in perfect English, then she switched to Swedish again and spoke to Ingrid.

"These are our English friends," said Ingrid.

The receptionist reverted to English.

"Please forgive me for assuming you were English. I should perhaps explain that we don't have many English guests and I need to practise my English as often as I can. How nice to be able to welcome you to Leningrad. We have a beautiful city and I hope you enjoy your stay. Please ask at the reception if there's anything you need— anything at all."

Lars, meanwhile had read his telex. He stood for a while, thinking.

"Not bad news, I hope," said Ingrid.

"Yes, in a way—we may have to fly to Berlin tomorrow. My secretary in Stockholm is waiting to hear from us— yes, my dear, you too, I'm afraid. We have to go to Berlin to discuss final arrangements for the Adlon contract. The DDR officials are getting jumpy, they usually do when the unexpected turns up—terrified of making decisions, I suppose."

He turned to us.

"I'm afraid this evening may be our last evening together. I have to phone my secretary for details, but she's already booked us into the Adlon for a couple of nights, so it must be important. I'll ring Stockholm first, then I'll ring Lufthansa and see if we can get a direct flight tomorrow morning."

Ingrid looked really fed up.

"So sorry, dear—I know you were looking forward to a few days in Leningrad, so I'll keep the room open until we get back. We'll only be away for a couple of days, but, unfortunately, our friends will have left Leningrad by the time we return. Perhaps you'd like to invite Joanna up to our room to freshen up before dinner."

"Be as quick as you can," said Ingrid, "I'm starving and you know how long they usually keep us waiting in the restaurant—and how about Denis?"

"Perhaps he'd like to stay here while I make the phone calls, it shouldn't take long."

"He might prefer to wait in the bar, then you can give us a ring from there and we'll come and join you."

They took the lift upstairs and I asked Lars where the bar was.

"Try the little girl in reception—you know, the one who gave me the telex—she's attractive and game for anything if you play your cards right."

I wondered how he knew she was game for anything, but I did as he suggested and she actually came with me to show me the way.

"I'd love to stay and have a drink with you, but I'm afraid I'm on duty this evening—perhaps another time."

What a relief! I counted my dwindling stock of roubles and ordered a large scotch and soda in the hope that it wouldn't be too expensive. The barman, discreet and observant, seemed to know what I was thinking and quickly put me at my ease.

"Any currency will do," he said casually, "German marks, English pounds—even American dollars if necessary. We have a Beryosca shop in the foyer, so the usual rules of currency exchange don't apply here either."

His English was perfect. He and the receptionist were obviously language graduates, hand picked for such a prestigious hotel.

I was about to order another scotch when Lars arrived.

"Two large ones," he said to the barman.

"Now then," he said, "progress report—I managed to book two seats on the first flight to Berlin tomorrow morning. My secretary says the Adlon is quite near the border and our contract to refurbish the hotel is on a knife edge. The Adlon was once Berlin's most prestigious hotel and is still a popular (even if unofficial) meeting place for entrepreneurs from east and west. People have no idea how much cross-border trade goes on under the counter."

"Did you get the contract because Sweden has always recognised the DDR?"

"Good heavens no—cross-border divisions usually sort themselves out, sooner or later. It's nothing to do with hostility and everything to do with supply and demand. Tourism is growing on both sides of the Iron Curtain and, with the exception of the USA and England, the Cold War exists mainly in the imagination. What a pity you English prefer to go along with America instead of us, but that, of course, is up to you."

"Another thing," I said, "these Beryosca shops—don't you think it's unfair that we can buy anything we fancy here while Soviet citizens are not even allowed in? This bar, for instance, with bottles on the shelves from all over the world—malt whisky, French cognac and so on— luxuries you never see in any Soviet shop or department store. Don't tell me you think that's fair?"

"Of course it's not fair, but life isn't fair—and never

has been. It's high time we learned to understand other countries and their problems—and that includes the Soviet Union. Most of us may not agree with their system, but they're doing their best to promote equality, even though they don't seem to be doing very well at the moment. We can only hope that, given time, things will improve. Meanwhile, all this talk of Cold Wars and Iron Curtains is not at all helpful and only increases their paranoia. Their great experiment has considerable merit and may even prevail, but remember—you can't make an omelette without breaking eggs."

The phone rang.

"Yes, Mrs Lindstrom, your husband is here—with an English gentleman."

"Sorry, dear. I thought you said you were going to ring when you were ready—we were waiting for your call."

The dining room was at the far end of the main building and all four walls were hung with original tapestries of the founding of Saint Petersburg in 1703. The room had obviously been a lavish banqueting hall at that time and traces of its former glory still lingered.

"This room is all that's left of the original hotel," explained Ingrid. "It's so old that we weren't allowed to touch it when we refurbished the rest of the building— and remember, everything depicting Peter the Great is sacrosanct in Leningrad."

She raised her voice.

"I only hope he had better service than we're getting tonight."

This did the trick straightaway and waiters appeared as if by magic. They swarmed around our table and produced gold-embossed menus, then they retreated to a safe distance to await our pleasure.

"Before we order," said Lars, "there's one thing you have to remember—never order anything from the menu unless it has a price against it. You will notice that only very few dishes are actually priced. This has nothing to do with extortion, but because meat and chicken are not always available. The printed menu is intended to impress, their guests, but you order an unpriced meal at your peril—however long you wait and however many bottles of Stolichnaya you consume, your order will never arrive. No one takes the trouble to explain why unless you thump the table and make a fuss. The only exception to this golden rule is fish, which is caught locally and is not on ration. To save time therefore, perhaps we should ask the head waiter what fish he would recommend for this evening."

He flicked his fingers and a waiter came running.

"Please bring us a bottle of your best white wine—and please ask the head waiter to spare us a moment of his valuable time."

The fish was excellent and we had a most enjoyable meal, followed by cognac, for which Lars insisted on paying.

"Think nothing of it—I charge it all to expenses anyway. Look upon it as a little going-away present from your Swedish friends. Ingrid and I have so enjoyed your company, as we hope you have ours. Perhaps one day, when Germany is reunited and the DDR less paranoid, we shall be able to meet at the Adlon and be presented with a menu which actually means what it says."

Joanna burst into tears.

"I can't bear it," she sobbed. "Why are politicians so stupid?"

She didn't say anything more—we knew exactly what she meant.

Lars rang for a taxi. We exchanged addresses and promised to write, but I think we all knew it was the sort of thing one does on holiday—too many uncertainties lay ahead.

The taxi arrived and the women were inconsolable.

Lars did his best to appear nonchalant.

"That's the trouble with women," he said. "Too emotional by half."

We waved goodbye and blew kisses through the back window, but it wasn't until we turned the corner that Joanna stopped crying and regained her composure. She smiled through her tears.

"Ships that pass in the night?"

"Probably."

There was nothing else I could say, so I put my arm around her and she snuggled up. How vulnerable she was—perhaps we all are when we say goodbye to people we love.

Five

Only two days left.

If truth be told, the thought of the journey ahead was quite daunting. We'd made good friends in Leningrad and, if we hadn't had to pay in advance for our Moscow hotel, we might even have stayed put for the rest of our holiday. Yoddy was safe and sound, the Kirov was superb and Leningrad was a lovely city, so why bother to leave? Perhaps the problem was the journey itself. A voyage into the unknown should be an important part of a motoring holiday, so why the apprehension?

Perhaps it had a lot to do with the uncertainty of driving anywhere in the Soviet Union. How many miles to Moscow? How would Yoddy face up to the journey? What would happen if she broke down or ran out of petrol? How many days or nights until help arrived? Would our insurance papers cover accidents and repatriation, et cetera.? I took refuge in a motto that I remembered from my school days—the only useful thing I ever learned in my three horrendous years at one of England's stately public schools before the war. It was a simple slogan—a mantra, almost—but it has since stood me in good stead, whether it involved a problem to be solved or, as at present, the known or the unknown. Although the risky option was, for me, completely out of character, I can't remember ever having had cause to regret it. The slogan 'Nothing venture, nothing win' has helped time and time again to overcome my natural reluctance to go for it.

We found our German friends already going for it when we met them at breakfast. They'd obviously risen at the crack of dawn to stake their claim to the window table before anyone else got there first.

"Here come the capitalists—you should be staying at the Europa."

"As a matter of fact, we had dinner there last night."

"There, I told you so, Inge—our food isn't good enough for them."

"Quiet, Hans, don't be so rude."

"Perhaps a glass of champagne to remind you of last night?"

We hesitated. They'd given us champagne last time— and here they were again, generous to a fault. Germans always are, especially on holiday.

"Come on—it won't kill you."

"All right then, just a small glass."

Joanna drained her glass in one gulp.

"There, Inge—that's the way to drink champagne, you should try it one day."

"Moderation in all things," said Inge primly.

Joanna changed the subject.

"Our Swedish friends invited us to dinner last night—they're leaving this morning."

"Is that the couple who joined you for breakfast yesterday?—the ones with the tarty car in the car park?"

"No, the tarty car in the car park is actually ours."

"There, Inge—I told you they were bloated capitalists as soon as they arrived."

We got on fine after that. They said they were staying for several days, so we arranged to meet them again for breakfast the next morning.

"Any time will do, we usually spend a couple of hours here—best place in the hotel."

"Thanks a lot—see you tomorrow then."

We went down in the German lift this time and it was a definite improvement. In no time at all we were stepping out into the lobby, where a girl in a smart, blue uniform stood, waiting for the lift. Her face seemed familiar and she smiled when she saw us, but I couldn't place her at first.

"Mr and Mrs Hilton?"

Then I remembered—it was the same wretched girl who had had been so insolent to everyone—the receptionist who'd caused all that trouble. Surely it couldn't be her—or could it? What a transformation! Without doubt, it was the same girl.

Hilde Trotte smiled sweetly.

"Mr Ostrovsky asked me to give you this—he said to tell you it's hot off the press."

It really was Hilde Trotte—actually smiling, too. Boris must have given her a reprieve and a crash course on how to make friends and influence people—nothing much wrong with her English, either.

"Mr Ostrovsky said you usually had breakfast on the third floor, so I was waiting for the lift to bring the programme up to you when the doors opened and there you were."

"Thank you, Hilde—we really appreciate that—and please thank Mr Ostrovsky, too."

We looked at the programme. It was indeed hot off the press—a special anniversary programme for Igor Stravinsky, born 1882. The Kirov Ballet were performing two of his finest works—*The Fire Bird* and *Petrushka*—to celebrate his anniversary. Joanna had always wanted to see *The Fire Bird*—a particularly demanding ballet being presented tomorrow night, which would provide a wonderful climax to our memorable week in Leningrad. Meanwhile, his beautiful ballet, *Petrushka*, would enchant us tonight.

The programme also included details of his monumental and revolutionary ballet, *The Rite of Spring*, which was to be performed by the Bolshoi in Moscow next week.

Thanks to Stravinsky's friendship with the impresario Diaghilef, *The Rite of Spring* had become a landmark in the history of Russian ballet, ignoring as it did the usual conventions of harmony, rhythm and form. We were glad to read all about it and we decided then and there that it gave us yet another reason for going to Moscow.

Joanna was even more specific.

"There," she said, "we now have two good reasons for going—Madame Greteskaya and *The Rite of Spring*, in that order."

I couldn't help wondering whether Stravinsky would have approved of her priorities.

We went to the Heritage again and had another lunch in the little open-air cafe Ingrid had found, tucked away in the courtyard. We had an equally delightful meal and the proprietor joined us for coffee afterwards. He told us that the Leningrad authorities welcomed initiatives like his, not officially of course—that would be too much to ask—but certainly unofficially.

"You have to remember the ground rules," he said. "Firstly, you get to know the right people, then you find a secluded location—somewhere where people come across you almost by accident, then you remain small and, as far as possible, inconspicuous. It also goes without saying that you must have sufficient capital to ensure a regular supply of foreign currency, otherwise your suppliers might be less than enthusiastic."

I took the hint and paid for the meal in foreign currency, whereupon he produced a bottle of DDR brandy.

"Try this," he said. "Cheaper than French cognac and quite as good."

We must have drunk half the bottle between us, before, mindful of the importance of sobriety when watching classical ballet, we decided that enough was enough. We thanked him effusively for his hospitality and, before we left, assured him we'd never divulge anything he'd said until the Soviet authorities had bowed to the inevitable by deciding that, whether they liked it or not, private enterprise was here to stay.

We sat by the river in the hot autumn sunshine, cooling off before taking a taxi to the Kirov for an evening with *Petrushka*.

"Did you enjoy *Petrushka*?"

Our German friends seemed well informed when we met them for breakfast the next day—they'd obviously been doing their homework.

"Yes thanks," said Joanna. "We're really looking forward to *Fire Bird* tonight."

She gave them our programme to have a look at and I seized the opportunity for a quiet word with the waitress.

"Tomorrow," I said, "is our last morning and I would like to buy our friends some French champagne before we leave. They'll probably be here first, so please make some excuse when they order their usual—say another dozen bottles are on the way and will be delivered in the next half hour, which should keep them happy until we arrive. Please bring in our special champagne as soon as we arrive, with an ice bucket and seven glasses—six for our table and one for the old lady outside."

I gave her a handful of roubles.

"Please pay for the champagne with this and keep some for yourself. It's important to keep it a secret as it's a farewell present for our friends."

"Time you stopped flirting with that waitress."

Joanna, covering as arranged, gave me one of her looks and, suitably humbled, I crept back to the table.

"She's rather nice, isn't she?—speaks German, too."

"He always speaks German when he's flirting," said Joanna, scornfully. "He knows my German is practically non-existent, so I never know what he's saying. He never has any luck anyway, so I usually let him rabbit on and on until his fancy piece tells him to get lost. You know what middle-aged men are like—always fancying their chances."

"Did you hear that, Hans?"

"Yes, dear."

"I may take you to the ballet tomorrow if you behave yourself."

"Yes, dear."

I decided to change the subject.

"We're off tomorrow," I said, "but we'd like to come and have breakfast with you before we leave, then, if all goes well, we should be away soon afterwards.

"You can't leave until we come down to see you off—we've already had a bet with our friends as to whether that tarty car of yours starts first time or not."

"Of all the cheek—she always starts first time."

I was on the point of betting my remaining roubles when I caught Joanna's eye and thought better of it.

"See you tomorrow then. Thanks for the champagne. We shall really miss it—and you too of course, like a hole in the head."

They roared with laughter—whoever said Germans had no sense of humour?

Back in our room, the very thought of packing was infinitely depressing.

"I'd like to go on a river trip today," declared Joanna suddenly.

Trust her! We'd already agreed to spend the afternoon packing.

"But..." I began.

"No buts," said Bossy Boots. "Everyone else goes on river trips—why can't we?"

"Because...."

"Because you haven't planned for it, that's why. It's not my fault—I leave these sort of things to you, then, at the last moment, you decide to spend the afternoon packing."

"But we agreed yesterday..."

That was yesterday. She knows perfectly well that I don't want to waste our last day packing suitcases any more than she does and this is her way of ensuring that we don't. Who wants to pack anyway?—we can pack all night if necessary. She's dead right of course—holidays are for having fun. We'll remember our last afternoon in Leningrad for the rest of our lives and, memories being what they are, the river trip and the *Fire Bird* would eventually merge and, in years to come, we would tell our grandchildren about the real fire bird we saw in the distance.

"What's a fire bird?" they'll ask, and we'll say it's something very special you only see in Russia—and you don't even see it then unless you're very, very lucky.

The hotel minibus took us down to the river. We went all the way down as far as the Winter Palace and returned just in time for Stravinsky's *Fire Bird*. How fortunate we were—and how boring our last day would have been if Joanna's sure instinct hadn't prevailed.

"You won't believe this," said Hans when we arrived for breakfast, "we've been waiting hours for our champagne and they keep telling us it's on its way, but it still hasn't arrived—would happen on your last morning, too."

"Never mind," I said. "It'll do you the world of good to abstain from alcohol for a change."

They'd reserved the special window table and their friends had already joined them.

As soon as we sat down, our champagne arrived, with seven glasses and a red rose.

"There must be some mistake," said Hans. "Why the rose and seven glasses?"

The waitress looked at us, smiling nervously.

"Never mind," I said, "it's here now—who's going to open it?"

"So," said Hans, "German champagne's not good enough for our capitalist friends. I always knew they'd go one better when they had a chance."

The waitress struggled with the cork and out it came. She tried to give me some change and I asked her to bring another bottle instead. The rest of the room stopped eating and listened, while Hans made a short speech.

"Our English friends," he said, "are leaving today. They have decided to educate us on the merits of French champagne. That of course remains to be proved—and the sooner the better as far as I'm concerned. We notice, by the way, that they've had problems counting the number of glasses required for six people. This may well reflect the standard of maths teaching in England, but, be this as it may, I would like, on behalf of my wife and our friends, to thank them for their generosity and friendship—we shall miss them like a hole in the head."

Everyone laughed at the joke—my joke, incidentally.

Inge was more perceptive.

Perhaps," she said, "the roses and the extra glass are intended for a special lady."

"Indeed," said Joanna.

She led the way out of the room and into the corridor and they followed her like a flock of sheep. The old lady saw us coming and gave a friendly smile. Never had so many people come to greet her. It wasn't her birthday and it certainly wasn't Easter, so why on earth all the fuss?"

Joanna took her by the hand and gave her the red rose, then she gave her a hug and a kiss. I gave her the glass of champagne and we all sang Happy Birthday, over and over again until we were almost in tune. The old lady looked totally bewildered, then she sipped the glass cautiously and her eyes filled with tears. She drained her glass and looked around.

"Tak," she said, "tak tak." Her voice rose to a squeak and she blew a kiss through gnarled, bony fingers.

Hans gave her a greetings card. We had written 'Best wishes to our dear friend' in several different languages. The waitresses, who were very fond of her, insisted on their own greetings to 'The Heroine of the Revolution', so we signed that as well. They told us that they also gave her a greetings card at Easter to celebrate the most important day in the calendar of the Russian Orthodox Church.

"We have to go now," said Joanna. "Give us a couple of hours, then wait for us downstairs—we promise not to leave until we've proved that Yoddy always starts first time."

We were running late, but we finished packing at last and I left Joanna to do the finishing touches while I went to fetch Yoddy. Boris had unlocked the gate of the car park and there she was, waiting patiently, none the worse for her incarceration. She spluttered a bit when I pressed the starter button, but she soon roared into life and I drove her round to the front entrance.

I found a porter and we brought the luggage down in the lift and stowed it away in the boot, then I went upstairs to fetch Joanna. She was sitting on the bed, looking miserable.

"I keep thinking of that dear old lady," she said quietly. "I'll probably end up like her in another thirty years or so."

"Never mind," I said, "I'll buy you a red rose and a bottle of champagne, then, if I'm feeling up to it, I'll have my way with you."

"That's what worries me," she said. "Forget about it—and don't think about it now either—we've got a long journey ahead of us and you haven't got that much energy at the best of times!"

We left the little room where we had been so happy and, on our way to the lift, we passed the dear old lady, who blew us a final kiss.

"I shall miss her a lot—and our German friends."

Joanna makes friends with everyone and she always misses them dreadfully when we have to leave.

We went down in the lift for the last time, through the lobby and out through the main door. Joanna gave a squeal of excitement when she saw Yoddy waiting for us at the bottom of the steps.

"Doesn't she look smart?—all washed and polished too."

The wash and polish had been a useful part of my deal with Boris, but I modestly took the credit—no point in telling her now.

"How clever you are—and where did you get the hot water? I never found any hot water when I wanted to wash my hair."

"Why didn't you ask?" I said smugly. "Initiative usually does the trick."

A small crowd had gathered at the bottom of the steps. It wasn't every day they saw such a splendid looking car. The Germans were there too, waiting for Hans to win his bet, and even Hilde Trotte was there to see us leave.

"She may look like a million dollars," said Hans, "but what's she like underneath?"

Inge, who'd only half heard what he said, glared at him suspiciously.

"Yes," I replied, "you can never tell with women."

Inge was not amused.

"I was only talking about the car, dear—I was wondering whether her performance was up to her appearance."

Hans looked straight at me. He needed my support and was waiting for me to say something.

"Don't be so straight-laced," I scolded Inge. "Can't you take a joke?"

Hans smiled with relief.

"Where's Boris?" asked Joanna. "We can't possibly leave until we've said goodbye to Boris."

"Shall I go and fetch him?" asked Hilde.

"Yes please, if you can—tell him we're just going, but we wouldn't dream of leaving without saying goodbye."

"Better still," I said, "tell him we haven't paid the bill yet—that will smoke him out."

Joanna went to the kiosk across the road and bought some flowers, then she waited at the top of the steps until he came out, blinking like an owl in the bright sunshine. Before he knew what was happening, she gave him a smacking great kiss and presented him with the flowers.

The kiss left a bright red lipstick smear on his cheek, clearly visible to everyone watching.

"Fancy that," remarked someone. "I wonder what his wife will think of that."

I didn't even know that Boris had a wife, but, come to that, I didn't even realise that Joanna used lipstick—perhaps she kept it in her handbag for special occasions.

We opened the car doors and wound down the windows, then I pressed the starter button. Dear faithful Yoddy started immediately, smooth as silk, no hesitating or spluttering. I pushed in the choke and she ticked over so quietly that we could hardly hear the engine.

"There, I told you so—she's stopped already."

"Want to bet?"

"How much?"

"Ten dollars too much for you?"

Hans handed me a ten-dollar bill and it was then that I made him listen to the almost imperceptible hum of her finely tuned engine.

"Quiet, everyone," I proclaimed proudly. "Listen to a good car ticking over, the car of the future. Cars like this will be all over the place in ten years time—and you won't even know what's hit you."

Boris came down the steps, lipstick smear and all, and gave Joanna a kiss through the open window.

"Goodbye, dear," he said. "Any time you get fed up with that husband of yours, just come and see me—we can do with someone like you to liven the place up."

He gave Hilde a quick smile. It was only a fleeting glance, but I had a feeling she'd be around for some time. She wouldn't be leaving in a hurry—not yet anyway.

"You've got lipstick on your cheek," said Joanna. "Ask Hilde to wipe it off for you."

We waved goodbye, the crowd cheered and, with a thin trail of smoke spiralling from her exhaust, Yoddy pulled away, quietly and unostentatiously.

The crowd continued waving until we turned the corner and it was only then that I remembered we'd left our road map in the breakfast room. Too late to turn back now, but no matter—we'd buy another one when we got to Moscow.

We drove around for a while until we picked up the ring road. We passed several filling stations, some long abandoned, with rusty petrol pumps and broken-down lorries, others with long queues of cars and trucks, patiently awaiting their turn.

"Look out for the signposts to Moscow," I instructed.

Joanna, expert in the Cyrillic alphabet, could hardly fail to see them.

"*Mocba*," she said brightly, "I haven't seen any *Mocba* signs yet."

"Perhaps signs don't look the same in Cyrillic," I suggested.

"Of course they don't, I'm allowing for that—*Mocba* is Cyrillic for Moscow."

We pressed on and the traffic thinned out. We should be getting to the end of the ring road soon and, as far as we could remember, *Mocba* was due south. Sure enough, the road ahead swept round to the south and we were on our way.

More by luck than judgement, we were on the main road to Moscow at last, but our euphoria didn't last long.

Six

We'd only gone a few miles when speed restriction signs suddenly appeared—40, 30, 20, 10, STOP. There was a sizeable hump of concrete across the road, so we had very little choice. We looked around and saw a low-lying concrete building with pill box windows. Two powerful police motor cycles were parked nearby and were the only outward signs of supervision, but, when we looked around, we saw two pairs of binoculars trained on us from the roof of the building.

"What are we supposed to do now?" asked Joanna.

"Put on your best smile, sit tight and wait—this is probably one of the dreaded road blocks I've heard about—stopping places to enable Big Brother to keep an watchful eye on everyone travelling between Leningrad and Moscow."

We stayed put and, sure enough, a police officer in uniform soon appeared. He strolled towards us and saluted.

"You have a nice car here," he said in German, "A nice Japanese car."

He looked at our papers and frowned.

"Would you please wait here while I show these documents to my superiors."

No use complaining.

We waited for what seemed an age, then a door opened and another man with a revolver of some sort strolled across.

He too saluted.

"Your papers are in order," he smiled, "but I'm afraid you cannot go any further, as this is not an authorised tourist route."

"But...but we're going to Moscow."

"Quite so, but you should have been told that this route is now closed to tourists, as it passes through a prohibited area. You will have to return to the Leningrad ring road and turn right, then take the first turning on the right. It is a longer way round, but it will get you to Moscow eventually. I wish you a pleasant journey."

He watched while we turned back towards Leningrad, then he waved in a friendly manner as I stuck my arm out of the window and gave him the V sign. I certainly didn't feel all that friendly towards him, although Joanna felt differently.

"You shouldn't have done that—he's only doing his job."

"That's the excuse everyone makes—and not only in Russia."

I looked at my watch—an hour gone and we were still on the outskirts of Leningrad. What a ridiculous country—why on earth couldn't they make up their minds and decide where we were allowed to go and where we weren't. We soon reached the ring road again and took the first turning on the right. It wasn't much of a road, but we pressed on for half an hour until I noticed that the road was getting narrower and grass was growing in the middle—a sure sign of very little traffic.

We stopped to have a look. There was mud everywhere and, whatever else it might be, this country lane was certainly no main road to Moscow. The only encouraging signs were a few wheel marks in the mud, so the road had to lead somewhere.

"Doesn't look too good," I said to Joanna. "What do you think?—shall we go back or shall we grit our teeth and carry on?"

"You're the driver—you decide."

"Tell you what, we'll carry on for another half hour and hope it doesn't get worse. If it does, we shall have to return to Leningrad with our tails between our legs."

The road got even worse and we found ourselves driving through a forest of birch trees—hundreds and thousands of young silver birches, all exactly the same.

"These aren't birch trees," said Joanna. "More like spruce trees, if you ask me."

"I didn't ask you, actually."

Trust Joanna to make that sort of comment. I envied

her uncanny ability to ignore everything except when it suited her to say something.

"You do realise, don't you," I continued, "that we're completely lost."

"Look," she said, "just ahead on the left."

Changing the subject again—then I saw it myself, a red notice board with white lettering, so we stopped to have a look.

"Why not go over dear and see what it says, you're the Cyrillic expert—remember?"

With some reluctance, she opened the door and squelched through the mud towards the board. It looked like a signpost of some sort and it might give us an idea where we were. She climbed on the bank for a closer look and scratched her head.

"What's keeping you?" I called.

"Do shut up—I think the first word is 'Comrades', but I'm not sure of the rest. It says 'beware' of something or other."

I got out and took a photograph. Was it my imagination or was it already beginning to get dark? We'd wasted an awful lot of time and I had a nasty feeling that we wouldn't make Moscow that night. We might just as well have stayed in Leningrad and left early the next morning, but it was too late now.

We got back into the car and faced up to the first real crisis of our holiday.

"Well," she said, "what are we going to do about it?"

"I really don't know," I said. "We can't turn round here and our only hope is for a truck or cart to come along and show us the way. Trucks and carts obviously come by from time to time, so there's always a chance of a friend in need. Why don't you go and have another look at the sign?"

"I'd rather not," she said. "It definitely says 'beware' of something."

"Perhaps it says 'Beware of wolves' or 'Beware of bears'. Perhaps they hide out in the forest while they wait for the next troika."

"What's a troika?"

"A sleigh or cart, with three horses abreast."

"Oh, ha ha, very funny. It's no laughing matter, you know—besides, I'm hungry."

We sat in silence and I looked at my watch—six hours since breakfast and three hours since we left Leningrad. It was later than I thought and, even if help did arrive, we couldn't possibly get to Moscow before midnight—far too late to find our hotel.

It was then I heard, or thought I heard, the rumble of a heavy truck coming up behind.

"Quick, Joanna, you're the one to wave him down, drivers always stop for you."

She jumped out of the car and ran towards the corner, waving frantically.

A huge truck loaded with timber rounded the corner towards her. The driver was obviously in a hurry. He was driving much too fast and the heavily laden truck was swaying from side to side. He jammed on his brakes as soon as he saw Joanna and the truck slewed, skidded and ground to a halt with only inches to spare. The driver—a tall, middle-aged man with a Communist Party badge—jumped out of his cab and shouted at Joanna, then, as soon as he saw Yoddy blocking the road ahead, he ran towards me, while Joanna—badly shaken, but otherwise unharmed—ran past me and jumped into the car. I opened the door and, almost in tears, tried to comfort her.

"Stop grizzling," she scolded, "I'm perfectly all right. The driver's coming towards us now and he may decide to help us if you're nice to him."

Tricky one, this. The driver was in a hurry and all he wanted was Yoddy of the way so he could carry on, so I had to decide quickly what to do about it. Any driver who can come round a blind corner at fifty with a heavily laden, ten-ton truck, then jam on his brakes, skid in the mud and throw the truck sideways to avoid killing a woman less than twenty yards away in the middle of the road, should be congratulated, so I decided to congratulate him on his fantastic pit stop.

He seemed completely unconcerned—emergencies like

this were probably all in the day's work. He strode towards us and I saw him eyeing the shallow bank. I knew only too well that an experienced driver would get by in no time—he'd back off a few yards, rev the engine, ram in the gears and throw the truck at the bank, missing us by inches if we were lucky, then he'd be away in no time and we would have lost our only chance of help.

I had to think quickly. I pulled the catch and opened Yoddy's bonnet just in time to lift it and peer inside. I've never yet met a skilful driver who wasn't interested in cars and this driver was no exception.

He stopped and said something, so I took a chance and spoke to him in German.

"Japanisches Auto," I said.

"Das hab' ich gedacht."

We'd made it—even Joanna stopped sulking, though he still ignored her.

"Wir haben uns total verfahren und meine Frau ist todmüde," I said, "wäre es möglich, dass wir hier in der Nähe übernachten könnten?"

He was a man of instant decision.

"Komm mit zum nächsten Dorf und wir werden 'mal sehen, was zu tun gibt."

He picked up a stone and pressed it against Yoddy's windscreen.

"Ich fahre ganz schnell, aber pass 'mal auf—fahr mindestens fünfzig Meter hinter mir—wegen Steinschlag, verstanden?"

"What did he say?"

Joanna's curiosity got the better of her as Yoddy pulled over to let him pass.

"We're to follow him," I translated, "but not too close,

because stones thrown up by his huge wheels could break Yoddy's windscreen."

"He seems a nice man after all, even though he didn't take much notice of me."

The driver scraped by and shot off, wheels spinning in the mud, then he slowed and waited for me to flash my lights, then he accelerated violently before shooting off again. I remembered what he'd said about stones hitting the windscreen, so we kept our distance. As he gathered speed, his huge tyres began to throw up mud and stones and some of the smaller stones flew towards us, bouncing on Yoddy's bonnet and hitting her windscreen. He was now driving flat out and I almost lost sight of him, but we held our own and Joanna began to enjoy herself.

"I didn't realise you could drive as fast as this," she said.

"I can when it's necessary," I said, modestly, "though it rather cramps my style when I have a valuable passenger on board."

"Now you're making fun of me."

"Wouldn't dream of it, but I'd be in serious trouble if I arrived in Moscow without you—they'd almost certainly send me to Siberia."

I glanced at the petrol gauge, which was ominously low—so low that I wondered whether I should flick my lights to warn him, but decided against it—he might carry on without us. Then, mercifully, he started to slow down and we came to a clearing with a little cottage on the left. He drew up beside it, jumped out of his cab and, without knocking, opened the door and went inside.

We stopped behind him, got out to stretch our legs and looked around It was already getting dark and there was no sign of life anywhere, but we did see another signpost—a real one this time. Straight on for Gorky and, at long last, right for *Mocba*. It was only then I realised how desperately tired I was. The uncertainty and strain of having to follow a ten-ton truck for fifty miles at speeds of up to sixty miles an hour had taken its toll.

I badly needed a rest and even Joanna, after her initial excitement at the speed of the chase, had had more than enough for one day, so, even if it meant sleeping in the car, here we were and here we would stay.

Poor Yoddy had had a rough time of it too. She was covered in mud and several small stones had pitted her bonnet. Not only that, but she badly needed petrol and almost certainly oil for the four-hundred mile journey still ahead. We waited for what seemed a lifetime until the cottage door opened and the driver came out with an older man. They spoke quietly together, then the older man greeted us in surprisingly good English.

"My friend says you would like to stay here if possible."

"We would be most grateful if we could."

"I'm very sorry, but we're not allowed to offer hospitality to foreigners without permission."

I tried again.

"My wife is tired and she's not feeling very well."

"I would like to help," he replied, "but we only have two rooms and they're not really suitable for guests."

Joanna gave him a pathetic smile—and she wasn't acting.

The driver was getting restless.

"Must be off now," he said. "It's getting late and I've got a load of timber to deliver before dark."

I wanted to thank him somehow, but he was a man

105

of few words and obviously didn't like sentiment, so I followed him to his truck and we shook hands.

He pointed at the signpost.

"I go straight on, but you take the right fork tomorrow— it joins the main Moskau road in less than an hour and it's another four hours after that."

He gave Joanna a smile, then he jumped into his cab, started the engine and wound down the window.

"Look after the lady," he said, "and try not to get lost again."

He was a proud man as well and the last thing I wanted to do was to insult him by offering him roubles, but I wanted to give him something. I suddenly remembered my bet with Hans before we left Leningrad—perhaps he wouldn't mind a ten-dollar bill.

I reached up and we shook hands again through the open window.

"Vielen Dank für alles," I said in my best German.

He looked at the ten-dollar bill in his hand and grinned.

"Danke, auf wiedersehen."

The huge wheels skidded in the mud and gripped the road, then, with a final wave, he was away.

Joanna had obviously succeeded where I'd failed—she often does.

The old man was all smiles.

"My wife and will be delighted to offer you our hospitality for the night. My name is Kuprin—Felix Kuprin—and my wife is Dinara."

He spoke perfect English and I congratulated him on his fluency.

"Dinara has taken your wife indoors—she was cold and tired, poor dear, and they've already got some soup on the stove. Perhaps, before we join them you would park your car under those trees—it will be safer there."

He seemed quite concerned about Yoddy, so I did as he suggested and followed him inside, where he introduced me to Dinara. She was laying the table and Joanna was stirring the soup.

"They seem to be getting on like a house on fire," said Felix.

The cottage had a large stove in the middle and they were busy preparing borsch. Dinara ladled out four huge bowls of soup and Joanna cut a huge loaf of homemade bread, then we sat down and, after a short prayer, tucked into a tasty evening meal.

We were very hungry and the soup was delicious. We all had second helpings and mopped our plates up with bread, then Felix fetched a bottle of vodka and we drank a toast to our English friends and their magnificent yellow car, then another to Felix and Dinara, special friends who had welcomed us into their home in our hour of need.

"That reminds me," I said. "Our case is still in the car—perhaps I should fetch it before it gets too dark."

Dinara hesitated.

"Your car can still be seen from the road—wouldn't it be better to drive it further back under the trees?"

The penny finally dropped. Of course—I remembered Aram telling us the unwritten law of survival in the Soviet Union—'never come to the attention of those in authority'. Two foreigners in a small village would probably pass unnoticed, but a bright yellow Japanese car parked overnight?—that was quite another matter.

I backed Yoddy further under the trees, collected the

cases and returned to find them hard at it and the vodka bottle half empty.

"Felix was the village schoolmaster before he retired," said Dinara. "He has plenty of time to spare now and still gives English lessons—in fact, his older pupils often come here for extra lessons."

"You sure they don't come for your borsch?"

"Perhaps that too."

"You know perfectly well that's why they really come," said Felix, smiling.

We'd almost finished the bottle before Joanna began to flag.

"Right," began Dinara. "It sometimes gets a bit chilly at night and when we have visitors, which isn't often, we open the door behind the stove to let the heat warm both rooms. Tonight, if you don't mind, we shall leave the door open. We shall sleep this side and you and your husband will sleep the other side."

"What a good idea," replied Joanna. "Of course we don't mind."

We fell asleep almost immediately. We must have slept the clock round because it was quite light when we awoke. We heard chickens clucking and cockerels crowing.

"Listen to that," said Joanna. "Russian cocks crow just like ours—what a pity we don't all speak the same language—it would make wars more difficult to wage and, with luck, so many people would refuse to fight that they would soon be a thing of the past."

"Perhaps," I murmured.

If only politicians spoke the same language—that would be a good start.

The samovar was on the boil and Dinara was cracking some tiny eggs, ready for frying.

"Good morning!—Did you sleep well?"

"Like logs," murmured Joanna, sleepily.

"Why like logs?"

"Don't know really—that's what we say in England."

"I must remember that," said Dinara. "Felix speaks such good English that, when we speak English together, I can never tell him anything he doesn't already know."

He was outside feeding the chickens, and she called to him.

"We're waiting like logs for you to join us for breakfast."

"You wait," she told us, "he's sure to correct me when he comes in."

"We sleep like logs," he said when he came in, "we never wait like logs."

"See what I mean?"

They told us the nearest garage was only a few miles away—fortunately on the road we'd be taking anyway—so that was the petrol and oil sorted.

We packed our things and I backed Yoddy up to the front door, while Joanna stayed inside, writing a little note thanking Felix and Dinara for their kindness and hospitality.

They came out to take a last look at Yoddy, so I went inside to fetch Joanna.

I found her sitting at the table, pencil in hand.

"There," she said, "that should do the trick."

She had written a little note—'Thank you so much for coming to the rescue in our hour of need—you are true Samaritans and we shall always remember you with love and affection. Denis and Joanna.'

She had placed her new lipstick on top of the note.

"Isn't that rather an inappropriate present?" I asked.

"Not really," she countered. "Dinara and I were talking last night while you menfolk were snoring and she told me about her daughter Kristina, who is a hotel receptionist in Gorky. She has, according to Dinara, all sorts of modern ideas and has experimented with lipstick, so I showed Dinara my lipstick in its silver container and she said she'd try to find one like it to give her. I suddenly had an idea—why not give her mine? It's a new one. I hardly ever use lipstick except on special occasions, but I brought it with me this time to impress the Kirov until I realised they only used stage make-up, so the only recipient so far has been Boris, who I feel might have been less embarrassed without it."

I gave her a hug and we were having a final look around when I saw a small pile of roubles on the table.

"Glad you left them something useful—how much?"

"Haven't a clue."

"What d'you mean 'haven't a clue'?"

"Well—how much would you have left them?"

"I really don't know."

"Well then—you haven't a clue either, so we're quits."

We went outside to find them still admiring Yoddy.

"Give my love to Kristina," said Joanna.

"She's coming home next week. Gosha sometimes brings her to and fro—that's how we met him originally. He's German, you know, captured during the war and sent to Siberia for ten years. He didn't want to go back to Germany after that, so he settled down in Gorky and married a Russian girl. He's a good driver too—comes by twice a week with timber from Archangel. Doesn't speak much, but he's got two little girls of his own and he's usually glad of a rest and a cup of tea by the time he gets here."

So that's why Gosha spoke German—Gosha the survivor—the driver who helped us in our hour of need, the Samaritan who stopped because he had to and led us to his friends Felix and Dinara, who took us in and cared for us.

The world, we thought, is full of Samaritans and we often don't realise how people help one another.

The time had come to leave and Joanna, as usual, was heartbroken, so I pushed her into the car and, with a final wave, we were on our way.

"Do you believe in providence?" she asked.

"Not sure really—how about coincidence?"

"No—much more important. How about the three complete strangers who came to our aid at the very time we needed it."

"All we need now," I said, "is another stranger, who, according to you, should be just round the corner, waiting for us."

Miraculously, as I spoke, we came to a filling station and, not only that, it had two signs—one in Russian and the other in German.

Petrol at last as well as a sign in German—perhaps Gosha wasn't the only prisoner of war not to go home.

We drew up at a solitary petrol pump—an old-fashioned pump with a handle. There was no one to be seen, but we were encouraged by a little sign on the pump, which stated 'Deutsch wird hier gesprochen'. I was airing my superior knowledge of German to impress Joanna, when a door opened and a burly man in overalls appeared.

I remembered a little note in the manual which said that high octane petrol should be used for best performance. We had been told that there were two grades of fuel in the Soviet Union—92 and 96, so I asked him for ninety-six octane fuel.

"Niet."

Nothing daunted, I summoned up my best German and asked him if ninety-two octane would be all right.

"Natürlich," he said, "aber etwas langsamer."

He wasn't so sure about the oil, so I handed him the manual to look at.

He frowned and pointed to Yoddy's bonnet.

"Mach 'mal auf."

I opened up and he checked the dipstick.

"You need oil," he said finally, "better oil than we have."

"Never mind," I replied. "Top up with the best oil you have—and we'd better take a small can with us so that we can top up again if necessary."

He had a look at the engine, then he checked the radiator and the battery before closing the bonnet.

Now for petrol. His English seemed to improve as he turned the handle.

"Sorry about all this," he said. "We don't have mains electricity and we've been waiting three years for a generator."

"That's an awfully long time to wait," I ventured.

"You obviously don't know the Soviet Union. I haven't enough money to bribe the right people, so I have to wait until it's my turn to be connected."

Yoddy's tank was soon full, so it was time to broach the subject of washing and polishing. Rather to my

surprise, he seemed to like the idea. He beckoned to two
young children, who ran towards us.

"These are my sons," he said proudly.

He told them to fetch two buckets of water.

"Get some sponges too," he told them. " We'll try and
clean the mud off this car."

We all joined in and Yoddy was soon shining like a new
pin. I was relieved to find that yesterday's stones had not
caused as much damage as I had feared, so we forgot about
the polish. It didn't take Yoddy long to dry and, while
we were waiting, a pleasant young woman, came out with
a jug of lemonade and we all sat around talking until the
sun went behind a cloud and it was time for us to go.

The moment of reckoning had arrived. I only had a
vague idea how much it would all cost and I was agreeably

surprised when the bill arrived. Joanna checked it and we saw they'd forgotten to charge for the washing.

"Look," he said, "life in the country is worth more than money can buy, but the children get bored when they don't have enough to do and your visit today has been a real treat for them—and for us too. I've been servicing and repairing Trabbis and Skodas for so long that I've almost forgotten what a decent car looks like and your little car has shown me the future. It's we who should thank you for such an enjoyable morning."

"There," whispered Joanna, "now tell me that you don't believe in providence."

Seven

We joined the main Leningrad-Moscow road in less than an hour, glad to have survived the near disaster that had so nearly undermined our determination to press on. Joanna of course had made light of her terrifying experience, but I couldn't help wondering whether an adventurous holiday like this could ever be justified if it involved putting her life on the line. Why on earth had we brought Yoddy in the first place? It would have been so much simpler—and cheaper—to have flown to Moscow and travelled to and fro by train like most sensible people. We would have had an interesting and uncomplicated holiday—but then we would never have met Wally or Aram, never had the experience of a four-day luxury cruise, never gazed through the morning mist at the magnificent golden spire of Leningrad's Peter-Paul cathedral, never been arrested, never made friends with so many interesting people, never landed up in the middle of nowhere, never spent the night with Felix and Dinara in their little cottage, sitting around their stove with a bottle of vodka and waking up to the sound of cockerels crowing. All this and more—and we hadn't even arrived in Moscow yet.

"Don't forget Gosha, the good Samaritan," said Joanna.

"What?—that madman who nearly killed you?—or have you already forgotten?"

"I suppose you're cross with the road block people who made us turn back?"

I knew exactly what was coming next.

"You realise, don't you, that, if they hadn't turned us back, we'd have been in Moscow yesterday and we'd never have met Gosha or Felix or Dinara or that lovely garage family. If that isn't providence, I'd like to know what is?"

She was right, of course—she usually was—but it started me wondering why they'd turned us back when so many other cars had been waved through. It was almost as though they'd been waiting for us, but why?

"Of course," I almost shouted. "Why didn't I think of it before?—it's really so simple—we're obviously on a blacklist for having been detained in a prohibited area on suspicion of importing a car without a licence. However unfairly, we're certainly now being watched. How easy it is for anyone to find themselves in this sort of situation and, in a totalitarian country, how difficult to explain. Even if we complain, the very fact that we complain will bring us to the attention of the authorities yet again and we'll be hedged in with even more restrictions."

The traffic was heavier now and overtaking more difficult. Three-lane highways with cars overtaking in each direction inevitably risk head-on collisions with other lunatics, so I tucked Yoddy into the slow lane. Joanna went to sleep and I had plenty of time to think.

If we were on a blacklist, so were Wally and Aram. Even Aram, for all his bravado, would have had to resort to bribery in Georgia—and Armenia as well—before he would be permitted to cross their frontiers and, as for Wally, with any luck he might have managed to cross into Estonia before the Soviet frontier guards realised he was on the blacklist, though they'd almost certainly grab him when he left for home.

I did so hope we'd make Moscow without any more road blocks—they wouldn't dare hold up hundreds of cars and lorries on the main highway—or would they?

Yoddy made good progress and another four hours found us in the greater Moscow area. Joanna woke up and gazed at the monstrous tower blocks dominating the skyline. They overshadowed streets of old, traditional wooden houses, each with its own front garden.

"I know which I'd prefer," said Joanna. "Give me a wooden cottage with a front garden any time."

"How about the Moscow winter with its sub-zero temperatures?"

"That's what's wrong with you—you can't help looking on the dismal side."

The Hotel Rossia was a huge, rambling hotel near the centre, and, more by luck than judgement, we found it quite easily. They seemed to know we'd be arriving a day late and it was only after we'd gone up to our room that I began to wonder how they knew.

"Don't be paranoid," said Joanna, "you'll be finding Reds under the bed in no time if you carry on like this."

We were starting to unpack when the phone rang and the manager asked if we would like a visit from Miss Fyodorov. He said that she was the Intourist guide assigned to the hotel and added that she would be glad to meet us at any time.

"Of course—no time like the present—ask her to come up."

There was a knock on the door in less than ten minutes and there stood a vision of delight—fair hair, blue eyes, lovely smile—the lot.

"Mr Hilton?—I'm Natasha Fyodorov, the hotel guide. I believe the manager has just phoned you and you said it would be convenient for me to visit you now, so I came straightaway."

How gorgeous she was!

"Of course, Natasha—please come in. What a pretty name."

I looked in the mirror. Joanna was giving me an icy glare.

"Please meet my wife, Joanna—we've only just arrived, but we're glad to see you."

It wasn't my fault she was so beautiful, let's just say she was an unexpected bonus and leave it at that. I made an excuse to leave them to it and, by the time I returned, they were getting on fine.

"Natasha's given me some guide books and street maps and she's suggested we might like to go to the Moscow State Circus tomorrow evening. She's given me two tickets and she'll come with us if we like. Monday is her day off, but she'll give us a couple of tickets for the Bolshoi too if we'd like to go. They're dancing Stravinsky's *Rite of Spring* to celebrate his anniversary. She says the best way to see Moscow is from the river, so we could start tomorrow with a river trip."

"You're the boss," I said, "suits me fine."

They were getting on so well that we decided Natasha was just the ticket for our first few days—how fortunate to have met her so soon. Yoddy was safe and sound in the underground car park and she would help us enjoy the sights of Moscow without disturbing her.

We finished unpacking and Joanna, having slept in the car, was more than ready for sightseeing.

"It's Saturday night," she said, "let's go out on the town."

Our first impression of Moscow was of a huge cosmopolitan city—not at all like Leningrad. Thousands of people thronged the streets and the bars and cafes were doing a roaring trade. Despite obvious shortages, private enterprise seemed to be flourishing and we were impressed to see so many different races and ethnic types. What a diverse country this was—a huge country with over two hundred million people and a host of autonomous republics, stretching from the Baltic to the Black Sea and the Arctic Ocean to Siberia and Mongolia—a huge land mass spread over eight time zones and with people from widely differing languages, religions and ethnic backgrounds, all mingling here in Moscow on a Saturday night.

It was as if Moscow was a huge railway terminus, with people greeting one another in a myriad of strange languages. We were welcomed wherever we went. It was Saturday night, but we felt perfectly safe and we didn't see a single instance of racial prejudice. Despite the crowds, there was virtually no violence and we didn't see a police car or a police officer during the entire evening.

Sunday morning had the makings of a fine autumn day. We sat on the steps outside the Rossia and watched the street cleaners sweeping the pedestrian walkway leading towards Red Square. The thick morning mist almost obscured the sentry standing on guard and we wondered why he was there and what he was supposed to be guarding. The mist cleared, and we didn't see him again, but we saw the outline of the Kremlin and realised for the first time how close we were to the square.

"If you ask me," I said, "it's more than likely they've sent us to the Rossia so they can keep an eye on us."

"I didn't ask you," snapped Joanna. "Anyway, I'm getting tired of your conspiracy theory—why don't you just forget about it and start enjoying yourself?"

"I am enjoying myself—no need to be so critical."

It was such a lovely morning that we decided to go for a walk, so I went inside to hand in the key.

"Mr Hilton, isn't it?—I have an letter here from Miss Fyodorov—she asked me to let you have it and she also asked me to remind you that Sunday is a good day for sightseeing."

I opened the envelope to find two tickets for the Moscow State Circus, two tickets for *The Rite of Spring* and a little note from Natasha:

> "Dear Mr & Mrs Hilton, So sorry I can't come to the circus with you tonight—the hotel will book a taxi for you if you like. I'm going to visit my brother and I shan't be back till Tuesday, when I hope we shall meet again. Regards, Natasha."

I thanked the receptionist and went outside to tell Joanna.

"Natasha left this note for us—she'll be away until Tuesday."

Joanna, however, wasn't listening.

"Remember that sentry, the one who disappeared?— Well, I've a funny, prickling feeling he isn't really there at all, almost as though he's a phantom, an apparition."

"Don't be silly—probably a trick of the light."

The mist had cleared now, so we walked to Red Square and spent a pleasant two hours wandering around and watching the guards marching to and fro outside Lenin's tomb until, feeling the heat, we remembered the river trip which Natasha had advocated. We waited by the jetty until a boat came along.

The skipper asked for our tickets.

"Tickets?—what tickets?"

"Show him your circus tickets."

An English voice came to the rescue and I didn't stop to argue.

"Joanna—that envelope I gave you, show the man our circus tickets."

Joanna found them, just in time, and the skipper waved us aboard.

There was a lady with a little girl just behind us and I thanked her for her help.

"Bit of a scrum here," she smiled. "Usually is on a Sunday."

"But why show him our circus tickets?"

"You must be new here—the Moscow State Circus arranges boat trips for children and their parents every Sunday. We go down the river first, then we come back and get off at the circus jetty in time for the afternoon performance which starts at three."

"What a good idea," said Joanna.

"It certainly is—this is Millie, by the way."

Millie smiled and gave us an old-fashioned curtsy.

She was a bright little girl about six and Joanna gave her a kiss.

"Why don't we find somewhere to sit down?" suggested her mother. "I'm sorry, I should have introduced myself— I'm Ruth and I work at the British Embassy."

"How interesting," said Joanna. "Some people have all the luck."

"Nothing grand," replied Ruth. "I'm the cook and my husband is the butler—we've been here for nearly four years."

"That's what I mean. What an interesting life—how did you get the job in the first place?"

"Luck, really—we put an advert in *The Lady* four years ago, thinking we might be able to work together in some grand country house. The first reply we had was a mysterious phone call from London, asking us to go to go up for an interview, all expenses paid, so up we went.

"We had a long interview with a lady somewhere in Kensington and she asked us all sorts of odd questions about politics and so on. We told her we weren't interested in politics and she seemed to lose interest after that, although she was quite friendly. She gave us cups of tea and a cheque for £50 to cover expenses and said she'd get in touch with us in a few days.

"Then, a few days later, she rang again and asked us to go up for another interview. We had to go to an old farmhouse in Surrey this time and there was a distinguished-looking man there. They asked us lots of questions.

"How old was Millie? How long had we been married, et cetera, et cetera. Did we vote Labour or Conservative at the last election?

"My husband was getting a bit fed up by now and he said he didn't much care for any of them, but they didn't seem to mind.

"They just smiled and apologised for asking so many questions. They asked to see our references and then came the bombshell—would we like a job in the British Embassy in Moscow? Wouldn't we just!—so they then said that, subject to the usual formalities, Her Majesty's Government would like to offer us a trial period of twelve months as cook and butler, commencing in four weeks' time.

"The usual formalities involved a stringent medical examination and a form of contract which included the Official Secrets Act. They asked us not to discuss this with anyone, not even our friends, and, four weeks later, we found ourselves on a flight to Moscow—first class, too."

What an incredible story.

"How about Millie's education?"

"She goes to the Embassy School with children from other embassies. She loves it there and she's already learning the Cyrillic alphabet and basic German—more than I ever managed to do. The Embassy School is just behind the Kremlin and other embassies send their children there. She's made lots of friends from all over the world except America, which has its own school."

The river trip was great fun and we returned to the jetty in good time for the circus. It more than lived up to its reputation as one of the greatest in the world and Ruth told us they changed the programme every week so that people could have a combined river and circus trip each week if they wanted to.

"Not only that," she said, "schools can also join in and orphan children and single-parent families can have a day out without having to pay anything."

We came to the conclusion that, as far as Moscow was concerned, the Soviet welfare system was the tops. What a pity other countries were not always as caring as the USSR in looking after their orphans and underprivileged children.

We said goodbye to our new friends with real sorrow and Joanna gave Millie an extra-special kiss.

It was still early evening as, hand in hand, we strolled back to our hotel, content to be in Moscow at last.

The great cathedral bells were calling the faithful to prayer, while those of lesser faith went about their own business.

The thousands of people who had thronged the streets yesterday were nowhere to be seen and the noise and bustle of the previous night had been replaced by a Sunday stillness, although Sunday evenings in Moscow were obviously good for trade. Bars and cafes were already opening and we decided to round off a successful day with a coffee and perhaps something stronger to celebrate our first day in Moscow.

We felt at home as soon as we opened the door of 'El Cubano'. The proprietor greeted us cordially and led us to a corner table before producing an intimidating menu.

"Just two coffees, please."

"I thought you were probably English—how about a Stolichnaya to warm the cockles of your heart?"

"Where on earth did you learn that?"

He shrugged.

"We have a similar saying in Russian."

Aram had already introduced us to Stolichnaya, so vodka it was—and very nice too.

We had another coffee and a second Stolichnaya and Joanna succeeded in fending off several admirers, who distracted me by offering ridiculously high exchange rates for English currency, while paying her outrageous compliments at the same time. Mindful of the drastic penalties lying in wait for anyone rash enough to indulge in black-market transactions, I declined their generous offers and was reassured when Joanna also decided to preserve her virtue intact.

These encounters were, however, quite straightforward and there was no evidence of the drug peddling which was already starting to affect our social life in England. The black market here was their own currency and sexual transactions, both of which could be considered comparatively harmless when compared to the life-threatening drug scene in other parts of the world.

We had a final Stolichnaya and the proprietor ushered us to the door. He thanked us effusively and we promised to come and see him again before we left Moscow.

The hotel wasn't far away and we wandered across the road, watching families with young children out for a stroll—even the cars made way for them as they crossed the road and stopped halfway across for a friendly chat—perhaps there was a special Sunday evening truce between drivers and pedestrians by way of thanksgiving for having survived the battles of the week.

The Rossia came in sight and Joanna stiffened.

"That figure in the distance—surely it can't be the sentry again—or is he still a figment of my imagination?"

I squinted my eyes against the sun, but I couldn't see anything.

"Perhaps he fancies you," I said.

"Well, I don't fancy him. You should know perfectly well by now that I dislike all men in uniform, particularly men with rifles."

"Only joking—let's talk about Madame Greteskaya."

"I thought we were going to visit her tomorrow."

"We don't know where she's staying and, even if we find her address, we couldn't just drop in on her without warning. Most people like to know when their visitors are coming—however welcome they are, it may not always be convenient."

"Hotel Russia—that's what they said at the Kirov."

"There isn't any 'Hotel Russia' in Moscow—I checked yesterday."

"Well then, they may have meant our own hotel—the Rossia."

"That," I said, "is more than likely."

"Why haven't they told us then?"

"Obvious isn't it?—How would the manager know we wanted to meet her?"

End of discussion—about time, too.

"I've decided," I said, "to start the ball rolling by asking the manager this evening. I'll see if he's in his office as soon as we get back to the hotel and, if he's there, I'll ask him if Madame Greteskaya is one of his guests. He'll know if she is or not and, even if not, he should know her address and, with any luck, her telephone number as well."

"You're really quite intelligent sometimes."

I smiled modestly and, for good measure, pointed out that the mysterious sentry seemed to have disappeared again.

"Never mind," I said, "he's probably some sort of Soviet Houdini."

The manager was in his office, so Joanna collected the key and went upstairs, while I stayed behind to have a word with him.

"Could you spare me a few minutes?—my wife has a letter of introduction to Madame Greteskaya and we wonder if she's staying here by any chance?"

"Let me see now."

The man was obviously playing for time.

"Perhaps it would be best to ask Miss Fyodorov—she'll be back tomorrow evening."

"We'd been so hoping to visit Madame tomorrow if it can be arranged."

He flipped, half-heartedly, through the hotel register, then suddenly seemed to change his mind.

"Ah, I remember now—Madame Greteskaya from Leningrad. She was a guest here three months ago. She had a suite on the third floor and many people came to visit her, but, after a few weeks, she decided to move. Miss Fyodorov made all the arrangements, so she'd be the best person to ask."

"How about her mail?" I asked. "Surely Madame left a forwarding address?"

"Let me see now—we might be able to find out from the telephone directory."

That was interesting—telephone directories did exist. The proprietor of El Cubano had told us there were thousands of telephones in central Moscow, but only a few directories. He himself had been waiting over a year for his own phone and, hopeful of bribing someone, he'd even gone to the telephone exchange, only to be told he wasn't important enough to have a phone just yet and any bribes on offer should be made elsewhere. While leaving, he'd even seen a Moscow telephone directory on the table, but he was told that these were only available to officially accredited hotels.

We'd found his story hard to believe, but, if he was right, the Rossia would certainly have one tucked away somewhere and I would soon find out. I followed the manager into his office and watched him open his safe.

He extracted a slim volume bound in red leather and with the single word 'Mocba' embossed on the cover.

Sure enough, there she was—'Greteskaya, Madame'. Her telephone number was there, but no address.

"I'm sorry about the address," said the manager. "I should have remembered that addresses are not given in the directory—we'll have to wait until tomorrow to phone the special address access department at the telephone exchange."

"Would it be possible for me to telephone from here to ask if we can come and see her tomorrow, then she can tell us where she's living and we can get a taxi?—it can't be all that far."

The manager shrugged his shoulders.

"Please help yourself."

He handed me the phone and I dialled the number.

A man answered the phone in a pleasant, well modulated voice.

"Do you speak English?" I asked.

"Of course."

"My wife has a letter of introduction to Madame Greteskaya, who I believe is now staying at your address. We would be grateful if we could come to see her tomorrow if possible."

"One moment please. What time would you like to come?"

"Any time really—perhaps tomorrow morning if that's convenient?"

I heard a whispered conversation.

"Could you let me have your names, please?"

"Denis and Joanna Hilton, from England."

More whispering.

"Of course, Madame will be delighted to meet you. Shall we say tomorrow morning for coffee—about eleven?"

"That would be splendid—and your address?"

The manager handed me a pencil and I wrote it down.

"Marco Polo Presnya—is that sufficient?"

"Of course, the taxi drivers know us well and it's best to take a taxi anyway—public transport is so unreliable. Thank you for ringing and we look forward to meeting you tomorrow."

I replaced the receiver, thanked the manager for being so helpful and asked him how much I owed him for the call.

He didn't reply, but he looked worried—almost as though he'd done something wrong—so I didn't ask him again. Instead, I asked if he would mind booking a taxi to take us to Marco Polo Presnya tomorrow morning.

"Of course—what time shall I say?"

"How long d'you think it will take?"

He wasn't sure, so I asked him to book the taxi for ten o'clock and we left it at that.

I thanked him again and I was just leaving when he called after me.

"Please tell Madame and her friend how much I enjoyed having them here and how sorry I was when they left."

So he did remember Madame after all. I wondered why he'd been so evasive when I first asked him. Perhaps he'd been instructed not to talk about her, but to wait until Natasha decided what to do.

Of course—that was it. He'd been told not to interfere in anything other than the smooth running of the hotel. Everything else was Natasha's responsibility. I realised at last exactly why she was here. She wasn't just an Intourist guide, she was an informer—someone who kept an eye on guests and reported their movements to her superiors. She was the one who kept an eye on Madame Greteskaya and everyone else, including ourselves, who had come to the attention of those in authority. The authorities needed to know where we were and what we were doing and she was the one who told them all about us.

The taxi arrived bang on ten and off we went. The driver knew exactly where to find Marco Polo. He said it would take about half an hour, so we asked him to give us a short sightseeing trip first.

"Ah," he said, "that's what we call the scenic route."

"That's right," I replied. "We might as well have our money's worth."

He looked puzzled at first, then he laughed.

"You English have an interesting sense of humour. I lived in England for a while and you can't help joking about practically everything, even money, but we know only too well that money is no laughing matter—it's deadly serious. Sensible people know this. Whether we like equality or not, money is scarce and tremendously important in the Soviet Union, but I still love the way you make light of it or at least the way you pretend it doesn't matter all that much. 'Having your money's worth' is a half-joke in England, but it certainly isn't here."

We were enjoying the conversation and we were quite sorry when he drew up in front of a large, seedy-looking hotel.

"Marco Polo," he announced proudly. "Our voyage of discovery is over."

I paid him and added a hefty tip.

"I hope you don't think I'm undermining your dignity of labour if I add a little extra?"

He laughed.

"A little extra might do just that, but I'm all in favour of a nice large extra."

We shook hands and he drove away. Quite the philosopher, I thought, but then—taxi drivers usually are.

Eight

We walked up the path and I rang the bell.

There was a shuffling noise from inside, then the door opened and a tall, distinguished looking man greeted us.

"You must be Mr and Mrs Hilton—Madame has been so looking forward to meeting you, please come in."

He was wearing carpet slippers, but his athletic build belied the image.

"Please follow me."

He raced upstairs at a speed we found difficult to match and threw open a door, with Joanna doing her best to follow. She had an armful of flowers for Madame, who stood there on the threshold, almost in tears. They were already embracing by the time I got there and, in her excitement, Joanna had dropped the flowers, which were strewn all over the landing, neglected and half-forgotten.

Formal introductions were out of the question, so I bent down and began to pick them up.

"Don't worry—I'll pick them up later. I'm Sergei by the way—Madame's constant companion."

"I'm Denis, and the lady locked in Madame's embrace is my wife, Joanna."

We stood there, looking through the door, filled with wonder at the sight of two grown women, crying like children. We both knew their first meeting was bound to be emotional, but we weren't exactly prepared for the outpouring and the floods of tears.

They calmed down after a while and Joanna produced the special programme which she'd promised to deliver.

"Here's a special programme for you—it's been signed by all your Kirov students. They send their love to you and Sergei. They told us how much they missed you and

how they all longed for the great day when you would come back to them again."

Madame Greteskaya stared at the programme through her tears.

"Look!" she said. "The photograph on the cover—is that really me? Why didn't they tell me?"

"They never told anyone," said Joanna. "The Ministry of Culture wouldn't have authorised the programme if they'd known."

"How do you know all this?" she asked. "Please tell me everything."

"Look inside the programme first," said Joanna. "Read what they've written, all the messages they've sent you."

She clapped her hands in delight.

"So they haven't forgotten me, how wonderful—now tell me everything."

Joanna told her about the awards, the champagne, the speeches and the enthusiasm.

"They drank toast after toast to you and Sergei—their joy and inspiration. They can hardly wait for the great day you return."

She clapped her hands again.

"Did you hear that, Sergei?—you too."

She and Joanna were crying again now, so Sergei picked up the flowers and arranged them in a vase, which he placed on the table in front of them. This seemed to have the desired effect, and they stopped crying for the first time since we'd arrived.

"There," she said, "Sergei thinks of everything, don't you, dear?"

She sat down at the table and had another look at the programme.

"Ah—here they are—Tatyana and Mischa, two of my best students. They've written something too, but what dreadful writing—I do wish they'd learn to write properly."

She started crying all over again, but Sergei put his arm round her and, in a gesture which spoke worlds of their love for one another, whispered in her ear, "Would you like a cup of coffee, dear?"

She looked up and smiled and then, for the first time, she saw me standing there.

"I'm so sorry," she said. "Please sit down—Sergei, you should have introduced the gentleman as soon as he arrived, how very impolite of you."

Sergei grinned, obviously used to being blamed.

"This is Joanna's husband, Denis—he's brought her all the way from England to meet you."

"How wonderful. I'm Irena and this is my partner, Sergei. You obviously know that we've been banished from the Kirov, but I don't expect you know why—let's sit round the table and we'll tell you all about it. Sergei will make the coffee and I'll do the talking.

"It all started when we took the Kirov to England at Easter last year. The tour was a huge success, but, unfortunately, we had two defectors. First to defect was Mariya. She went to the toilet as soon as we got to Heathrow and we never saw her again. Our two minders (or baggage handlers, as the authorities prefer to call them) were furious. They accused us of collusion, took our passports away and bundled us into the hotel bus. It wasn't until we got to the hotel that we found out what had become of her.

"We met an American girl in the bar. She seemed to know who we were—she came up and introduced herself as soon as we arrived. She told us she'd met Mariya in the toilet at Heathrow by arrangement and she'd given her an American entry permit and a ticket for the next flight to New York. Mariya already had her own passport, so everything was fine and she was already on her way to America. 'Good news,' she said; 'Mariya is safe and well and, at this very moment, halfway across the Atlantic— free at last.'

"We were so excited at the news that we started singing 'God Bless America', but, at that very moment, one of our minders came in for a quiet drink. I tried to explain to him that we were just practising, but I could see he didn't believe a word of it. Sergei, with great presence of mind, introduced the American girl to him. He said she was a dancer with the New York City Ballet and that, through her, we were hoping for an invitation to dance with them next year, but that only made matters worse.

"They watched us like hawks after that, so it was all the more surprising when, at the end of the tour and, at the very moment we were passing through customs, Mikhail, the timid one who wouldn't normally say boo to a goose, escaped. He broke away from the group and ran for it, then he leaped over the barrier and shouted in English that he claimed political asylum.

"There was a dreadful row when we got home. Our minders were summoned to Moscow to explain why they had allowed not one, but two dancers to defect so easily. They told a lot of lies of course—how we'd distracted them deliberately to prevent them from seeing what was going on until it was too late, so we too were summoned for a reprimand and they warned us that we would be held personally responsible in the event of any more defections while the Kirov was on tour."

Sergei arrived with the coffee and plonked it on the table.

"What's all this I hear about being personally responsible?"

"Only this year, dear—you haven't been sufficiently important until this year."

"Good job too—let's have our coffee first, then I'll tell them what happened this year—instead of being congratulated, I ended up by being blamed for everything."

"You'll have plenty to say—you usually do, so why don't we ask our guests to stay for lunch?"

They looked as us expectantly and I looked at Joanna.

"How kind of you—are you sure it's convenient?"

"Of course—Sergei will get the lunch. By the way, don't forget to ask him why he's wearing carpet slippers—it's really rather funny."

Sergei drank his coffee slowly, reluctant to embark on the saga of the slippers. He finally told us that, when asked by the Bolshoi, he sometimes went there to rehearse the *corps de ballet* instead of their usual teacher.

"Nothing special, but it's important for me to keep in practice and for them to realise that the Kirov can usually teach them a thing or two. Anyway, they'd been rehearsing *The Rite of Spring* for several weeks and their principal dancer was resting in preparation for the opening night— tonight, as it happens.

"*The Rite of Spring* is very demanding, so they asked me if I would stand in for him by demonstrating the superb dancing for which the Kirov was so rightly famous. I was naturally only too pleased, but pride comes before a fall. I landed heavily and broke a bone in my foot—only a little bone, fortunately, but enough to put me out of action for a few weeks."

He poured some more coffee and we made appropriate clucking noises.

"Now I've admitted my incompetence, I shall relate

to you the reason why I now share with Irena the doubtful pleasure of being held responsible for yet another disaster. What I did was actually a great success, but, through no fault of mine, it turned into a disaster—a disaster for which I'm quite unfairly having to take the blame.

"Irena has already told you that we were hauled over the coals after Mariya and Mikhail had defected. The official reprimand took longer than usual—three whole days, in fact. They said they didn't need me on the last day, so I gladly left her to face the music and spent the day sightseeing. We stayed at the Rossia of course and she was late back, so I went outside to see if she was coming. That's when I first noticed the sentry. I watched him marching up and down like a lost soul and I don't know why, but it suddenly gave me an idea for a ballet— a children's ballet for Christmas.

"Just imagine that the authorities have forgotten about him. He's still on the payroll, but no one ever comes to relieve him. Time passes and he continues his lonely vigil, wondering what has happened. Children wander by and bring him food, joining hands and dancing around him, singing old Russian folksongs, but the sentry remains steadfast in his box, ready for all emergencies. A new century begins and more children dressed in peasant costumes bring him bunches of flowers. The flowers grow and surround the sentry box with masses of beautiful blooms, then the children plant sunflowers, which grow to a great height until they cover the roof and the sentry disappears from sight.

"He emerges from time to time with his rifle at the ready, but the children continue to dance around without a care in the world and, for the first time, he smiles, secure in the knowledge that all must be well if the children were so happy—perhaps he could even join them. One freezing winter, with snow and ice thick on the ground, the children grab his rifle and chop it up for firewood, so he discards his old uniform and burns that as well to help them all keep warm.

"Free and happy at last, he links hands with the children and joins in the merrymaking. They all dance around in a circle and sing a hymn of praise to peace."

We were deeply moved by his description. The colours and the beauty he had conjured up filled the room. The coffee was getting cold, but no matter—what a wonderfully appropriate ending for a children's Christmas ballet.

"So beautiful," said Joanna. "Now I know why Irena insisted on your sharing the honours and why you're now both equally important—but why on earth should you be the villain of the piece?"

"Why indeed?"

Sergei shrugged his shoulders and, for the first time, Irena interrupted.

"Because that's just what he is—you'll never believe the fuss it caused. Would you be a dear, Sergei, and make us some more coffee?"

We waited impatiently for the next instalment.

Sergei brought in the coffee and we listened, enthralled.

"Anyway, Irena seemed to like it, so we took the idea back to the Kirov and the kids were thrilled to bits. They liked it so much that we put the idea to the trustees and they agreed with us that it was just right for their Christmas ballet, so we started the ball rolling straightaway. We told the designers and the scenery people that they had a free hand to start planning for Christmas. We gave them a rough budget to work on and encouraged the other principals to help whenever they had the time, then we got together with a few friends to discuss the feasibility.

"It looked promising, so we rough-timed the sequences and went hunting for suitable music—piano music would avoid the expense of having to drag in the orchestra on Christmas Day. We found something suitable almost immediately and, after a few weeks, the whole thing began to take shape.

141

"The scenery people and the costume designers did their best and the experts timed the first trial run, which of course was a disaster—rehearsals always are. The timing was all over the place and everyone blamed everyone else, but, after a hectic few hours, we began to see the wood for the trees and were able to start arguing about the choreography, then the scene shifters and the costume designers joined in and we spent ages deciding where the scenery should go and what costumes the children should wear. We couldn't start dress rehearsals for another four weeks and even these had to be scheduled so as not to interfere with the rehearsals for the main Kirov productions in the run-up to Christmas.

"Everyone worked hard and the kids were wonderful. The carpenters had built an imposing sentry box, which we placed centre stage, and Irena involved all her younger students with dancing and costume changes until they were exhausted.

"Then Irena and I decided on the timing for each sequence to enable the pianist to follow the score. We were cutting it a bit fine now, but providence was on our side and most of the music fitted beautifully first time. All we needed now was a convincing sentry. Our principal dancers drew lots for the honour and we decided on a somewhat undernourished dancer—tall and scraggy, but of military appearance —someone able to stand perfectly still for the best part of an hour before emerging to dance like a dervish for the finale.

"After some discussion the whole cast decided we should call it *The Sentry's Dream*, so we sent the programme off to the printers and still had time to distribute it in good time for Christmas. We sent it to the parents and guardians of all the students, together with a cordial invitation to join us on Christmas morning.

"The great day came and the whole thing was a huge success. We had invited our impresario friends over from Scotland and they were tremendously impressed—so impressed in fact that they immediately phoned their friends in Edinburgh, who came up with a brilliant suggestion.

"They spent ages on the phone and our friends made a list of everything they would need. They fully realised that they would have to find their own children, but that was part of the idea. They would present the ballet as a tribute from the children of Leningrad to the children of Edinburgh, who, despite the Cold War, had already been corresponding with schools in the Soviet Union.

"What they needed were the music, the scenery, the sentry box, the costumes, the pianist and as much help as we could give them, and they would do the rest. There was barely time to arrange all this for Easter, but it could just about be done, given sufficient goodwill on both sides and, if we liked the idea, they were more than willing to sign a statement of intent that we could send to the Ministry of Culture in Moscow for their approval and, as soon as they got back to Edinburgh, they would follow it up with a form of contract for our solicitors, which they could then send to Moscow for final vetting, together with a list of everything they needed from the Kirov and the amount offered for permission to stage the event and the facilities granted. Needless to say, the copyright would remain with the Kirov.

"The contract duly arrived and we were amazed to see how much they were offering. The authorities obviously couldn't believe their luck either, as they approved it straightaway and even authorised a low loader to collect the props from Leningrad and take them to Edinburgh."

"Sergei, dear—can we have a break now? Our guests must be starving."

No borsch this time, but real caviar.

"Caviar is not such a luxury as you may think," said Irena. "It's more or less the same price as most fish—a bit more perhaps, but not much."

She seemed anxious to reassure us that they enjoyed a good standard of living, although we knew full well that the last six months must have been difficult for them. The meal finished with more coffee and a cognac and we waited impatiently for the next instalment.

"They sent us a programme from Scotland and an excellent job they'd made of it too. The translation was perfect and we were greatly amused by the title, which had now been altered to *Lieutenant Blot—The Sentry Time Forgot*. Everything arrived safely and we sent them one of our carpenters and two costume designers to help sort out the scenery and the costumes. Unfortunately, at the last moment, neither Sergei nor I were able to go, although we were constantly on the phone to make sure that everything went according to plan.

"The Edinburgh publicity caught on like wildfire. Auditions were arranged in junior schools to find children of the right age who could sing and dance and the schools gladly allowed them to attend dress rehearsals, so, as Easter approached, *Lieutenant Blot* was uppermost in everyone's thoughts. Schools made block bookings and even the Soviet Consulate became involved. They were deluged with requests for tickets and we even had the Scottish daily papers rooting for us.

"Headlines abounded—IRON CURTAIN LIFTS AT LAST—CHILDREN BLAZE TRAIL TO SOVIET UNION. When asked to comment, the American Embassy in London maintained a discreet silence, although a spokesman said that, in his opinion, the whole thing was nothing but a typical example of insidious Soviet propaganda.

"The evening was highly successful and, to our delight, the Scottish papers were unanimous in their praise, although the Soviet Consulate struck an unexpectedly sour note. They issued a press statement to the effect that the Soviet Union was not amused by a ballet performance that ridiculed the sentries in Red Square who, night and day, guarded Lenin's sacred tomb. Furthermore, by portraying a sentry who abandoned his post and burned his rifle, the whole ballet was a nasty capitalist slur on the gallant Soviet army.

"We were thunderstruck when we heard what they'd written—and in a press release too—then the phone started ringing and we knew that the *coup de grace* from Moscow was on its way—a special car was coming to take us to Moscow for another reprimand in open court so that we could explain why we'd brought the Soviet army into disrepute. We took our solicitor with us and he reminded the court that the Ministry themselves had authorised the contract and had even supplied a low loader to take the scenery to Edinburgh.

"This only served to annoy our interrogator. He told us they had authorised a ballet entitled *The Sentry's Dream* and asked us who had authorised the change of title.

"Our solicitor did his best—'It's a children's fairy tale,' he said. 'All sorts of things happen in fairy tales. The whole of Europe is talking about our ballet—you should be glad to have other European countries on our side.'

" 'How dare you tell me what I should think,' he shouted. 'I'll have you struck off if you say that again.'

"He must have suddenly realised he'd overstepped the mark by threatening a solicitor at a public hearing, so he rose to his feet and announced a short recess.

" 'You'd better come with me,' he said to our solicitor. 'It's time we had a little talk.' I remember thinking this might be a step in the right direction, as our solicitor said afterwards that he apologised immediately for having threatened him before reading out a list of complaints which had been made against the Kirov, some dating back several years. The complaints were as follows: failure to promote the virtues of the Soviet Union on more than one occasion; inciting Kirov students to prefer freedom and the western way of life instead of the ideals and discipline of the Soviet Union; giving interviews to the press without authority; encouraging students to defect to the West and aiding and abetting defectors; ignoring numerous directives from the Ministry of Culture—and so on. The list was endless, but, rather surprisingly, it made no mention of the ballet which had caused the rumpus in the first place.

" 'I asked him about this,' he said, 'and he told me in confidence that, as far as he was concerned, the whole thing had been blown up out of proportion and was nothing more than a storm in a teacup. He'd already advised the Ministry to drop the charge to avoid making themselves look ridiculous.'

"However, he said that the Ministry had already decided to bring the Kirov to heel. The Bolshoi had been complaining for years that their brighter students were regularly being poached by the Kirov and this could not be allowed to continue.

"He then suggested a compromise, which, he said, was in everyone's interest:

1 All charges in connection with *The Sentry's Dream* and *Lieutenant Blot* to be removed from the file and future productions authorised.

2 Irena Greteskaya and Sergei Shelekhov to apologise for their continual failure to notify the Ministry of Culture of Kirov ballet productions.

3 Irena Greteskaya and Sergei Shelekhov to be banished to Moscow and placed under house arrest for a period of twelve months.

" 'And if my clients refuse?' our solicitor asked.

" 'Then the matter is out of my hands, but you should remind them that this is their last opportunity to redeem themselves and, if they refuse, their democratic rights will be withdrawn and they will become enemies of the state—and we all know what that entails.'

" 'Then I accept these conditions on behalf of my clients.'

" 'Good, I thought you would. Here is a shorthand note of this discussion. Please return to your clients and inform them that you have accepted these conditions on their behalf. The formal agreement is already being typed by my secretary and will be delivered to you shortly. Here is a declaration, which you should hand to your clients. It is an undertaking on their part that they will report to Comrade Fyodorov at the Rossia Hotel, Moscow, within the next two weeks, in return for which we promise that their house arrest will be supervised in a humane and reasonable manner.'

"And that," said Sergei, "was the start of our exile, although I really can't see why I should take the blame when the authorities themselves have admitted that they over-reacted."

"Of course you're to blame," said Irena. "It's high time you found out what a *bête noir* you are. It was your children's ballet which first brought us to the attention of those in authority and, if it hadn't been for all that fuss, we'd probably be still in the clear, but never mind, you're as important as I am now and you always wanted that."

"Not any more," said Sergei. "I'll let you deal with problems in future—always supposing there is a future."

"Of course there is," said Irena. "We've already survived for six months and in six months' time we'll be laughing. Just think of the party we'll have at the Kirov when we return."

What a lovely couple they were—and what a fantastic story. Just think—all over the Soviet Union, people longing for freedom are having the same sort of problems and they're being offered the choice of either doing as they're told or digging their heels in and having their legal rights suspended as enemies of the state.

We were grateful to them for confiding in us and we promised we would never divulge what they'd told us until the Soviet Union had decided that, even if they didn't agree with people who found it difficult to conform, everyone had equal rights.

Before we left, they told us why they'd left the comforts of the Rossia for the less comfortable surroundings of the Marco Polo.

"We told Natasha that the only reason we wanted to leave the Rossia was because we never had any peace there. *Pravda* had excelled itself before we arrived, with an entire page devoted to our exile, so, as soon as we arrived at the Rossia, a horde of photographers and other riff-raff were waiting for us outside. You can well imagine the headlines the next morning—MADAME GRETESKAYA AND LEADING DANCER UNDER HOUSE ARREST. As though that wasn't sufficient, the Moscow papers excelled themselves with lurid stories about our relationship and—even worse—told their readers where we were staying.

"That set the cat among the pigeons with a vengeance and, before we'd even unpacked, we were besieged with so-called 'well wishers', who kept saying how nice it was to be able to retire with a 'friend' at such an early age. We spent most of our first day getting rid of them and assuring the nosey-parkers that we had no intention of retiring—yet.

"Things got even worse after that—there were queues of stupid people, all waiting for a chance to gawp at us, and we felt more and more like animals in a cage."

Sergei, who usually quite liked being in the limelight, had felt the same way.

"Irena was particularly cross," he added, "at the constant references to myself as her 'friend', although I didn't really mind—I quite liked being a toy boy.

" 'His name is Sergei,' she shouted at them, 'and he's my lover.'

"We threatened to report them to Comrade Fyodorov for trespassing on government property. This got rid of some of them, but there were plenty of other morons to take their places and even the manager seemed powerless to do anything about it, so we decided to leave the Rossia as soon as possible.

"Natasha was sympathetic and said she'd do her best, but she warned us that there was a serious shortage of hotel accommodation.

" 'Never mind the luxury,' we said. 'Just get us out of here or we'll commit suicide.'

"Anyway, a few days later, Natasha brought us here to have a look. She said it was an old hotel that the authorities were waiting to renovate. Part of it was already in use as a school for handicapped children and they were looking for a caretaker to keep an eye on things until they had a chance of restoring the whole building. It was quite derelict in places and she apologised for its ramshackle state, but Sergei was longing for something to do—anything to pass the time—so we jumped at the opportunity and here we are."

Joanna looked at her watch.

"I'm afraid we have to leave now, but thank you again for a delightful day—and good luck for your homecoming. What a pity we can't be there to welcome you."

Our taxi drew up outside and took us straight to the Bolshoi—another celestial theatre, but even larger than the Kirov. We were entranced by the red and gold decor, the rich velvet curtains and the unmistakable legacy of Tsarist opulence as we sank into comfortable seats to await the experience of a lifetime.

Joanna, as usual, was spellbound, but I kept imagining Sergei showing off, leaping into the air and landing heavily. I tried to concentrate, but I found myself waiting with bated breath for some other poor unfortunate to do the same. Stravinsky's discordant music didn't help either and I decided that, given the choice, I would prefer to be watching Sergei's Christmas ballet than listening to Stravinsky's music.

After two hours and a number of successful leaps, we'd had enough. We slunk out during the second interval and went straight to our little cafe. It was still open and the proprietor welcomed us with open arms. He led us to a large table and introduced us to his friends. A pianist was playing Hungarian gypsy music and we felt relaxed and happy. We drank far too much wine and the proprietor produced a bottle of vodka at closing time to help us on our way.

We staggered back to the Rossia about midnight and there, in the moonlight, stood a solitary figure with rifle at the ready, waiting to be remembered—Lieutenant Blot, who else?

Nine

Natasha arrived as we were finishing breakfast. We waved to her and she came across to our table.

"Hope you don't mind if I join you—I've been travelling all night and I'm starving."

The waiter brought her bacon and eggs and she tucked in ravenously.

"Sorry about Saturday, but I'm glad you got the tickets—did you like the circus?"

"Great—and we had a free river trip as well."

"I forgot to tell you about the river trip, glad you managed it—by the way, did you like Stravinsky?"

"So-so."

We didn't dare confess we'd left before the end—perhaps we would when we knew her better. It was high time now to tell her about our visit to Madame Greteskaya, although it was more than likely that she already knew.

"We went to see Madame Greteskaya yesterday," said Joanna, casually.

We waited for her reaction, but she was as cool as a cucumber.

"I'm so glad," she said. "Did you meet Sergei, her partner? I rather fancy him. If I'd known you were going, I'd have taken you in my little car. It's virtually impossible to get there by bus, but there—I expect you took a taxi. How did you get to know her?"

"I had a letter of introduction from England," said Joanna, "and when we arrived in Leningrad, they told us she was living in Moscow, so all we needed was some detective work, a bit of luck and an intelligent taxi driver. Luck was on our side and we found them in. They welcomed us with open arms and even invited us to stay for lunch. What lovely people they are."

"You certainly deserved to meet them at last," said Natasha. "It must have been a memorable visit."

"It certainly was," said Joanna. "We told them we had two tickets for *The Rite of Spring* and we spent some time discussing it. She said that the dancing was out of this world."

"And was it?"

"Yes, in a way, although Sergei did complain that he'd broken a bone in his foot while he was standing in for their leading dancer."

"Yes, I heard about that—nothing too serious, I hope."

News certainly travelled fast and we resolved to be on our guard. Pleasant though she seemed, we had a shrewd suspicion that she was paid to keep an eye on everyone in the hotel and report everything they did. Our beautiful Intourist guide was almost certainly a police informer.

Seemingly satisfied, she carried on with her breakfast, though she couldn't resist a parting shot.

"I hope he's walking all right now."

"Yes—in carpet slippers, though Irena warned us that he was rather like a bear with a sore head."

Natasha smiled. The mention of carpet slippers seemed to reassure her that there was nothing sinister about our visit—nothing really worth reporting.

"Did you have a nice weekend?" asked Joanna.

153

"Yes—not bad, though I hate travelling overnight; it plays havoc with my make-up, and that's not all—I've now got to catch up with all the work I didn't do yesterday."

"Doesn't give much away, does she?" said Joanna after she'd gone. "She said in her note she was going to visit her brother, but she hasn't said anything about him."

"Probably a crafty weekend," I said. "I wouldn't be surprised if she had a lover tucked away somewhere—even spies have to relax sometimes."

"I wish you'd stop calling her a spy," said Joanna.

"Well that's what she is, isn't it?"

"I'm sure there's more to it than that—she may have had an important meeting."

"If you ask me, more like a secret lover."

We still had a bit of a hangover from last night, so we dawdled over coffee and spent the morning trawling through the guide books, trying to decide where to go.

The phone rang. It was Natasha again.

"Look—why don't we go sightseeing this afternoon? You haven't seen my little car yet, have you? It's a Zaporozhets and I'm very proud of it. It's manufactured in the Ukraine and my brother works in their new assembly plant at Brest Litovsk, on the Polish border."

"What a funny name for a car."

"It may sound funny to you, but you'll be impressed when you see it."

"What d'you call it again?"

"A Zaporozhets—my brother Viktor is an engineer and he says there's a huge waiting list of at least two years. I managed to jump the queue last year and there's quite a black market for them in Moscow. I've had all sorts of offers and I may even sell her soon and ask Viktor to jump the queue again and get me a new one."

So that was that—our afternoon planned and a free ride to boot. Perhaps Joanna was right. Lars had told us that all Intourist guides had to send in reports on motorists and hotel guests as a matter of course—there was nothing necessarily sinister about it. We remembered how helpful she'd been to Irena and Sergei—and to us as well—that too was a part of her job, the part she obviously liked best. Perhaps we should suspend judgement until we got to know her better.

We arranged to meet her in the underground car park at twelve noon and we had a look at her car before she arrived. It was certainly a sporty-looking car and I could well understand why she was so fond of it. The design alone was streets ahead of the dreary Russian and East German cars we'd seen up to now.

"So that's your wonderful yellow peril—what a lovely looking car."

Natasha's voice echoed in the vast, cavernous spaces of the underground car park.

I opened Yoddy's door and she jumped in before we could stop her.

"Gosh—Viktor would be really jealous if I told him I was sitting in a Toyota Celica. I told you he was an engineer, but he's a good designer as well and he was on the Zaporozhets' design team, which, as you can see, certainly knows how to design cars."

"How did you know our car was a Toyota Celica?— she hasn't been on the market all that long."

"Viktor and I are car enthusiasts. I was in London three years ago on a special crash course in advanced English and he got leave of absence to come and see me. They were already working on an improved model—still the same V4 air cooled engine, but with more leg room—so they gave him introductions to several car manufacturers and agents in England and we went to see them all.

"They were only too pleased to discuss their future plans—perhaps in the hope of a vast new market in the Soviet Union in years to come. Anyway, they showered us with leaflets and technical data, which we still have, so it was easy for me to identify Yoddy."

"How did you know we called her Yoddy?"

"Ah, that's a secret—anyway, it's such a lovely afternoon that, if you've no objection, I thought we might go for a drive in the country instead of boring old sightseeing. I'd like you to meet my grandparents and, while we're there, I'd like to discuss a few things which have been worrying me recently.

"You've obviously been wondering what I'm meant to be doing here and it's probably no accident that you went to see Madame Greteskaya while I was away, so I'll be glad if you'll bear with me a little longer and all will be revealed."

We jumped in her little car and she shot up the ramp and out into the street. She was a good driver, but in a hurry—almost as though she had finally made up her mind about something and was impatient to get on with it.

We were soon out in the country. She seemed to know exactly where we were going and we were impressed when she sailed right through the first roadblock with a wave of her hand.

"They recognise the car," she said.

We turned off the main road and she accelerated up a narrow lane.

"Don't worry," she said. "No one ever comes down here."

She'd obviously been here before—perhaps it was a one-way street.

"There's a small farm at the end. My grandparents live there and I come to see them whenever I can—ostensibly to buy eggs."

What did she mean, *ostensibly*?

The lane curved to the left, then—right at the end and almost hidden from sight, was a small farmhouse. They must have heard us coming, because the door opened and an elderly couple came out and waved.

Natasha slowed down and stopped beside them.

"Don't worry," she said. "These are my friends—I've brought them to visit you."

We shook hands and Natasha spoke to them in Russian, reassuring them about something.

"They're not used to visitors," she told us. "They've lived here all their lives and, apart from Viktor and myself, they don't really know anyone."

She introduced us formally.

"These are my lovely grandparents, Nikolai and Lyudmila Krylov. They've lived here for a very long time and, after the war, when my father was posted missing, my mother brought us here and we all lived together. Then, after my mother died, they looked after us during those dreadful post-war years, when hundreds of thousands of people died from starvation, malnutrition, and disease. They nurtured us and often went without themselves so that we had enough to eat.

157

"They sent us to school and college, where we both did quite well. Viktor qualified as a design engineer and was taken on by the Zaporozhets car company, while I went to university to study languages, mainly English and German. I got a first in English and went for an interview with Intourist. They decided my English was good enough to justify a further year in England—I think I told you about this—and, as soon as I returned, they put me on special duties—but that's enough for the time being."

The old couple stood patiently, waiting for a chance to have their say.

"Welcome," said Mr Krylov in almost perfect English. "My wife and I insist that you stay for lunch—nothing much I'm afraid, but it would be an honour to have you as our guests."

"Do you mind," asked Natasha, "if we stay outside for a little longer?—it's so lovely here after Moscow that we'd like to sit in the sun and chat for a while."

"Of course not—we'll call you when it's ready."

"Now," said Natasha, "it's high time I told you what's going on. I would have liked to have told you earlier, but it's so important that I had to ask Viktor first. I've already told you that I went to see him over the weekend, but I haven't told you why. We had a lot to talk about and, because I like and trust you, I just have to tell you what's going on—what we plan to do—or perhaps you'd rather not know—it's entirely up to you.

"I'll start by explaining that we in Intourist are coming under increasing pressure to tell the authorities of everything that goes on—and I mean everything. What started off as a *bona fide* tourist organisation has now become an vast instrument of oppression—a government-controlled network of spies, spying on one another as well as on tourists like you.

"It's got so bad that we're all having to tread a tightrope between our real job to promote tourism and our instructions to report everything to our lords and masters in the Kremlin—and I mean everything.

"As an example, you've just visited Madame Greteskaya and Sergei, who have obviously told you why they've been banished to Moscow. They were made to sign an agreement that they'd never tell anyone why they'd been banished, but it is of course inconceivable that you would have spent all that time together without them telling you the reason they were now living in Moscow. I should perhaps have stressed this in my weekly report, but I'm sick and tired of all this cloak-and-dagger stuff—all this nonsense is getting me down, which brings me to the next part of the story.

"Viktor too is now totally disillusioned. I've already told you he is a good designer. Well, twelve months ago, he was passed over for promotion because he wasn't a party member and, to encourage him to change his mind, they took him off engineering and put him on the production line. We had a long talk last weekend and I can now tell you what we talked about."

She lowered her voice and looked around. Joanna and I looked at one another—we both knew what was coming.

"This is the difficult part. Please remember that, if anyone gets to hear about this—anyone at all—Victor and I would almost certainly be sent to Siberia for at least five years."

We nodded.

"We're planning to escape, defect—call it what you will.

159

Fortunately for us, Brest Litovsk is almost on the Polish border and, even more fortunately, the huge shipyard at Gdansk supplies quite a lot of essential components for the Zaporozhets' production line. Viktor says they often run out of parts, which they're supposed to order from the main factory in the Ukraine, but these take so long to arrive that they're living from hand to mouth most of the time, so they're now allowed to order direct from the Gdansk shipyard. This involves sending a truck across the border to collect whatever's been ordered and my brother is one of the few people with sufficient experience to know exactly what's needed, so he usually goes along as well. It's quite a long journey and sometimes takes two or three days."

"And Sweden is just across the Baltic?"

"Exactly. We spent the weekend planning our escape and we've almost reached the point of no return. All we have to do now is to keep our mouths shut for a week or two and hope for the best. The really difficult part will be leaving our grandparents behind in the knowledge that we'll probably never see them again."

"Why are you telling us this?—is there anything we can do to help?"

Natasha smiled with relief.

"I was hoping you'd offer, but I'd never have asked— not in a million years. Quite a small thing really. We'd be ever so grateful if you would deliver a little note to our friends in Warsaw on your way home. They can help us get to Sweden as soon as they know more about our plans and this is the only safe way of letting them know what we plan to do. Anyway, that's enough for the time being—the final instalment will follow after lunch."

We looked at her, so young and courageous—prepared to give up everything for an unknown future.

We went into lunch to find soup on the stove and crusty, homemade bread.

Mr & Mrs Krylov soon made us feel at home. Their farmhouse reminded us somehow of the kind couple who had taken us in for the night on our way to Moscow. After lunch, Mrs Krylov suggested we might like to stretch our legs.

"Natasha, dear—show your friends round while we make tea—and don't forget to show them your room."

"This is my room," said Natasha. "They haven't been near it since I left home five years ago. It will always be my room—look, there are my old toys, untouched for years and my old photographs, still hanging on the wall. There's so much I shall miss."

We joined the old couple for a dish of tea before we left and they insisted on giving us a basket of large brown eggs. We said goodbye and they made us promise to call them Nikolai and Lyudmila next time we came, then they followed us out and waved us goodbye as the little Zaporozhets, wheels spinning in the mud, accelerated down the lane leading to the Moscow road and home.

"Now for the next instalment," said Natasha when we reached the main road. "How to sell my car and buy another one. I've already arranged with Viktor to get me one of their latest models and he's been allocated a new one from next week's production line. If all goes according to plan, I may even be able to collect it next week.

"Our plan is to defect with the new car and the cash from this one, so as not to be penniless when we get to

Sweden, but my problem now is how to sell my old car on the black market without being rumbled."

"I've got an idea," I mused. "I think I know just the place."

She stared in disbelief.

"What makes you so sure?—What do you know about our black market?"

"I didn't say I knew anything—I was only going to make a suggestion."

"Come on, then."

"That little cafe, not far from the Bolshoi—I think it's called 'El Cubano'."

"Don't say you've actually been there."

"Of course we have. The owner's quite a character and all sorts of interesting people go there."

Natasha blushed and kept her eyes on the road.

"I wouldn't dream of going to a place like that."

"Why on earth not?"

"It's—it's not exactly my idea of entertainment."

"You mean it's not respectable enough for you?"

Natasha stopped the car in a lay-by and appealed to Joanna.

"It's nothing to do with respectability—it's just..."

"I know exactly what she means."

Joanna, switching sides—just like a woman.

"There are limits," she said.

"Limits to what?" I asked, but they didn't answer.

"Please yourselves," I shrugged. "I'm sure the proprietor would help—he knows all sorts of people and he likes those who don't conform. Youngsters especially need to let their hair down from time to time and his little cafe is the nearest you've got to our all-night cafes in the west—even people of your own age like going there."

They didn't reply, but the reference to her own age group had obviously struck home and Natasha capitulated.

"Perhaps you're right—I probably missed out as a teenager and I'll have to start making up for it sooner or later."

"Why don't we go there tonight?" I asked. "We've nothing to lose and everything to gain."

"I'm certainly not leaving my car anywhere near that cafe—someone's bound to steal her and then where will we be?"

We returned to the Rossia and Natasha parked in her usual space.

"I can't go looking like this," she said. "I'll have to change first."

"Nothing too respectable," I pointed out. "Respectable girls stand out like a sore thumb in El Cubano—try going downmarket for a change."

"What d'you mean—downmarket?"

Natasha, undecided, turned to Joanna.

"Perhaps I could come to your room after I've changed and you can let me know what you think."

"Please be our guest," I said. "You're welcome any time—any time you like."

"Take no notice of him," sighed Joanna. "He always carries on like this."

We went to our room and Joanna put on her party dress while we were waiting for Natasha to arrive. She arrived at last. She was wearing a slinky red dress and she looked absolutely stunning— a bit tarty, maybe, but just right for an evening at El Cubano.

"Just the job," I said, admiringly. "Are you quite sure it's the first time you've been there?"

"Why do you say that?"

"No reason, but your sexy red dress is bound to attract the locals—they'll be all round you like bees round a honey pot and your main problem will be sorting the sheep from the goats."

"Meaning?"

"The sheep being those with real money and the goats being the usual shady bunch out to get you on the cheap, though even they might have a bob or two if you're lucky."

Ten

I pushed open the door and made a grand entrance, girl on each arm. There was a sudden hush and the proprietor rushed forward to greet his new guests.

He was so busy bowing and scraping that it wasn't until we were seated that he realised who we were.

"Oh it's you! I thought polygamy was frowned upon in England."

"This is my younger sister," said Joanna. "We don't usually bring her to places like this, so take good care of her and don't let her speak to any strange men, otherwise we shall think twice before we bring her here again."

The proprietor grovelled appropriately. He kissed Joanna's hand before turning to me, oozing charm.

"My name is Henry, sir—it is indeed a pleasure, sir, to make your acquaintance again. I'm eternally grateful to you, sir, for honouring my humble cafe by bringing me two such charming ladies. Please assure your charming wife and her equally charming sister that they have nothing to fear. You have no need to worry—your wife and Miss...? will be in safe hands."

"Natalie," said Natasha.

"What a beautiful name. I should have known that such a lovely young lady would have a name like Natalie."

"What about your own name?" I asked. "Who on earth decided to call you Henry?"

"I did," replied Henry. "I like English names—they're so...civilised."

He clapped his hands and the four-piece band, dressed in motley Cuban uniforms for the occasion, redoubled their efforts. It wasn't every night they had a high-class tart in their midst—they usually had to make do with whoever was left over at the end of the evening. Henry would produce the poor unfortunate girls for their inspection in the hope that they would take them home instead of payment and he'd probably dispel their initial hesitation by throwing in two or three bottles of cheap vodka so that he never actually had to pay them anything.

The Caucasian girls were usually the ones left over. Young, pretty and friendless, they had nowhere else to go and they'd be only too pleased to spend the night with them for a bed to sleep on and a few glasses of vodka. They would turn up at opening time, hoping against hope that they would meet their dream lovers during the evening, but all they usually got was a quick visit upstairs for a few roubles before it was time to leave, then Henry would offer them to the band, who, accustomed as they were to same old left-overs, perked up this particular evening at the possibility of a high-class tart for the night and played with renewed vigour.

The merrymaking continued unabated and even the high-class tart was beginning to enjoy herself. Couples gyrated around the dimly lit room, hugging and kissing. From time to time, a couple would go upstairs and reappear ten minutes later, flushed and exhausted.

"You must excuse me," said Henry. "It's nearly time for the anniversary—we have one every Tuesday."

He seemed uncertain which anniversary they were actually celebrating, but it didn't really matter—kebabs and Bull's Blood were on the house and that's what everyone was waiting for.

"Bull's Blood?"

"Sorry—I should have told you—the musicians are Hungarian gypsies and they love their special red wine. It's dry and heavy and comes from Kisvarda in Hungary."

"But I thought they were from Cuba."

"Far too expensive, but I really must go now and help my friend—he's in the kitchen with the kebabs and he's waiting for me to bring in the wine."

He pushed through the beaded curtain and returned almost immediately with a cauldron of thick, red wine, closely followed by a handsome young man with a tray of sizzling kebabs. Candles were lit and Henry called us to order.

"I give you a toast," he shouted above the din, "a toast

to the distinguished guests in our midst—may they return again and again to this oasis of freedom in the wilderness of Moscow."

We never did find out why Tuesday nights were so important and, as the evening progressed, it didn't seem to matter either. The Bull's Blood and the vodka flowed and it wasn't long before we completely forgot why we were there and what we were meant to be doing. I found myself dancing with a sexy Caucasian girl in a flimsy dress and nothing much else by the feel of it, while Joanna and Natasha played the field while they had the chance.

The climax came when Natasha, having finally decided who was to have the honour of purchasing her car, staggered to her feet and pointed towards the lucky man.

"Enrii!" she cried. "You're the one I want."

She swayed across the room and pinned Henry to the wall, then she grabbed him with both hands and pushed him through the beaded curtain. The last we saw of him was his terrified face—a stoat confronted by a weasel.

"Now you listen to me," we heard her command as they disappeared into the kitchen.

Everyone stopped whatever they were doing and there was a stunned silence. That gorgeous girl with Henry?—surely not.

First out was Henry's boy friend. He seemed extremely cross, which, given the circumstances, was, perhaps, only to be expected. He went straight upstairs and slammed the door.

They drifted towards the beaded curtain and listened, but everything was quiet—no squeals, no protests, no heaving and panting—not a sound.

Disappointed, the musicians resumed their efforts—it was nearly midnight anyway and they could always do with a bit of cash instead of the posh tart.

Suddenly the curtains parted and a dishevelled Henry emerged, blinking furiously, followed by Natasha, looking like the cat that had swallowed the canary. Henry looked around sheepishly—hoping against hope perhaps that their absence hadn't been noticed.

"Stolichnaya all round," he shouted.

Stolichnaya was for special occasions, so something special must have happened—but what?

Natasha waved to Joanna.

"Mission accomplished!" she shouted above the din.

Her delight at having sold her car was shared by those present, but for quite different reasons. Henry seemed to have scored at last—miracles did sometimes happen and they were only too happy for him as long as it meant Stolichnaya every night.

The merrymaking continued until midnight, when the band played their usual spirited rendering of the last waltz and crowded around Henry for their money. They knew from experience that the best time to get paid was when he was in a good mood.

With unusual generosity, he not only paid them the full amount, but also presented them with two bottles of vodka. On the strength of this, they invited two remaining Caucasian girls home for the night. Having failed to secure more affluent partners, they readily agreed—it was beginning to get cold and they had nowhere else to go.

We waited behind while Natasha and Henry wrote down what they'd agreed. Henry, relieved no doubt that she hadn't forced him to do the unthinkable, had readily consented to her terms and was beginning to recover his equanimity, although he did scold her quietly.

"I did so love the name Natalie—why did you have to go and spoil it?"

"What's wrong with Natasha?"

"Nothing—nothing at all."

"Thursday afternoon then—at the Rossia, about three."

They shook hands and she gave him a quick kiss, then Henry escorted us to the door and thanked us for coming. He kissed Joanna's hand with old-world courtesy.

"Please come again, when you can—and don't forget to bring your sister with you."

The taxi had a comfortable back seat and, with the door open, we pushed and pulled Natasha until she was sitting upright and there was room for us to sit down, then I told the driver where to go and off we went.

We heard a groan, followed by a sliding and a thumping noise, so we switched on the roof light and found Natasha asleep, lying in a crumpled heap on the floor.

"Let her be," I said. "She's had a hard day—let her sleep it off."

"She's not asleep," pointed out Joanna. "She's crying her eyes out."

Tears were streaming down her face, smudging her mascara. Gone was the veneer of confidence which had carried her through the evening and, in its place, a bewildered child looked at us accusingly.

"It's all your fault," she sobbed. "Fancy telling me you call your car Yoddy."

She gulped back the tears.

"The more I think about it, the more I realise that a car is not just a car, she's like a friend and, once you've given her a name, you can't bear to part with her— and now I'll never see Zappy again—and you're responsible."

Her words slurred and she gulped several times before continuing:

"I decided a few days ago to call her Zappy and, from then on, she's been as close to me as you are—and now I've sold her to a complete stranger—and it's all your fault."

She burst into tears again and Joanna was still trying to comfort her when we arrived at the Rossia.

The driver helped us out and helped us up again when we collapsed in a heap on the pavement.

"I'm so sorry," I said. "The ladies aren't feeling very well—I'll have to ask someone from the hotel to help us."

The driver had seen it all before. He gave a grunt and got back into his cab.

"Thank you," I said.

"Tak, Tovarich."

We struggled into the hotel and managed to get as far as the lift without attracting too much attention. Natasha was feeling sick and Joanna decided to take her up to our room to sober up.

She pushed open the door, staggered across the room and collapsed on the bed.

"I've heard of Reds under the bed," said Joanna, "but this is ridiculous."

We tried to move her, but she began to snore.

"What do we do now?" I asked.

"Nothing else for it," sighed Joanna. "We'll have to sleep three in a bed—and I'll sleep in the middle."

★ ★ ★

I woke up hours later and heard them whispering. It was still dark and I couldn't remember where I was—in a time warp perhaps, waking up in the middle of the night—was it really twenty years ago?—and finding Joanna, comforting one of our children. She had cuddled and reassured him then in much the same way as she was cuddling and reassuring Natasha now.

"It's not just Zappy," Natasha was whispering, "it's much

more than her—it's my lovely grandparents and my mother's grave and this beautiful city and all the friends I'll never meet again. I'm Russian and I love my country and I'm frightened at the thought that I might never be able to return."

As I listened, I suddenly knew what she was going through—what it must really feel like to have to leave your own country forever—and never return.

She was still sleeping when we got up the next morning, so we left a little note for her, hoping she felt better and suggesting she might like to join us for breakfast if she felt up to it.

We'd finished breakfast by the time she appeared. She'd been to her room to wash and change and she'd done her hair.

"That's better," I smiled. "You look almost human."

She laughed and gave Joanna a kiss and a hug.

"Thank you both for last night," she said. "I'm feeling much better now."

"So glad," I replied, "but perhaps you'd tell us why you're selling Zappy and buying another car? Wouldn't it be more sensible to keep Zappy and draw cash from your bank account when the time comes?"

"Three reasons—firstly, the cash we need will have to be in foreign currency, preferably German marks or American dollars, and the problem is that Soviet citizens are not allowed to deal in foreign money without special permission, which is rarely granted.

"Secondly, all employees of the state, which includes myself, have to open bank accounts and their monthly salaries are paid into their accounts. Intourist, for instance, pay my salary direct to the Moscow Narodny Bank and the account is regularly scrutinised. Any unusually large deposit or withdrawal is reported to the authorities and an investigation usually follows, which is the last thing I need at the moment."

"And the third reason?"

"Less important, but it might be useful to allay suspicion when the time comes. I've already told the manager that I'm going to sell my car and buy another one, so, if anyone asks him if he's heard any rumours about my plans, he'll ridicule the whole idea—after all, why buy a new car now if I'm planning to defect?"

We were filled with admiration. How clever she was, not only to plan her escape, but even cover remote eventualities.

Joanna, on the other hand could hardly wait to hear

about what had really happened at the cafe and why Natasha had chosen Henry instead of one of the wealthy sheep.

We waited patiently while she drank her third cup of strong black coffee.

"That's better," she said at last. "I'm still hungry, but I'm bursting to tell you about last night. I decided to find out first who had real money—not peanuts, but enough spare cash to buy Zappy, so I offered to sell myself to everyone I danced with. Most of them jumped at the chance until I mentioned my fee—one thousand American dollars for one night of love. I even offered a special weekly rate of seven thousand and hinted that this could include a limited amount of daytime dalliance if necessary—quite a bargain really.

"As you can imagine, the high cost of sin soon disposed of the hopefuls and I finally narrowed the field down to two—one I didn't fancy anyway and the other you already know—our very own Henry, who turned out to be the wealthiest of the lot."

She laughed at the thought.

"Funny I didn't think of him before. Most women know by instinct when they're looking for a wealthy man. A really rich man seldom flaunts his wealth, fearful of attracting the wrong sort of people—women, for instance, or tax authorities or, if he's that way inclined, unsuitable boyfriends. Henry of course was a sitting duck, ripe for the plucking. He already has a boyfriend, so, far from cheating, I was offering him a really good deal.

"From my point of view, I didn't have to go through all that ridiculous rigmarole about how much I charged et cetera, et cetera, so there were advantages on both sides. All I had to do was reassure him that I had no designs on his body—or, come to that, any other part of his anatomy—and, once he realised this, he was so relieved that I could have named my own price—so you see, it often pays not to go by appearances.

"He left me in the kitchen while he went upstairs to fetch the deposit (which, by the way, I haven't yet counted) and we shook hands. I wouldn't be surprised if his safe wasn't stuffed with enough Deutschmarks and dollar bills to sink a battleship or, perhaps more importantly, to buy two or three Zappys. From what he told me, he has several contacts who would be only too pleased to take Zappy off his hands, so I've probably done him a favour."

Joanna, who had pretended to be shocked, burst out laughing and we ordered a bottle of champagne to celebrate.

Natasha's eyes lit up.

"Champagne for breakfast?—how decadent."

She drained her glass and looked around to ensure that no one was watching, then she upturned her shoulder bag and a shower of banknotes fell out.

"Careful," I said. "Don't spoil good champagne with American paper money."

"The Americans call them bills—dollar bills—and you can help me count them if you like. There should be ten thousand dollars here, exactly half the amount our friend is paying for Zappy, with the other half due tomorrow when he comes to collect her."

"How about if he doesn't turn up?"

"He'll come all right. I've given him Zappy's registration documents as evidence of good faith, but they're useless without the registration book, whereas I've got his ten thousand dollars as well as Zappy, so I've got everything to gain and he's got everything to lose if he doesn't turn up tomorrow—does that make sense?"

We counted the dollar bills and stacked them neatly in fifties, then Natasha helped herself to a few and stuffed them in her handbag.

"I'm going to the bank now," she said, "to make sure they're genuine. Would you look after the rest for me until I come back? I know where to go and I'm sure my contact won't mind if I accidentally leave a fifty behind when I leave him."

"How about Henry?—how can he be sure that Zappy's documents aren't forgeries?"

"He can't, but I'm sure he knows where to find out. We Russians have learned a thing or two about survival in the last ten years."

I looked at Joanna.

"Actually, we'd prefer not to be responsible for all this money—why don't you leave it in the hotel safe?"

"No, that's the last thing I'd do. We Russians have a proverb, 'If I don't see it in my hand, it doesn't exist'— that's why we avoid banks and hotel safes like the plague. Joanna will look after it for me, won't you, dear?—you've probably always wanted to know what it feels like to have a fistful of money."

We were still arguing about who would be responsible for looking after the money when Natasha made the decision for us—she finished her coffee and left us to it.

"I'm off now," she said. "I'll be back in about an hour, then we'll take Zappy for a final spin round Moscow."

She was back in no time.

"Everything fine," she assured us. "Fortunately, I met my contact on the way in and he took me straight to his office. He peered at the bills through a special machine and confirmed that they were perfectly genuine, so I was on my way in less than twenty minutes."

"What time did you say Henry was coming tomorrow?"

"About three. We're meeting in the underground car park, which reminds me—I'd better move Zappy from her official parking space so he won't smell a rat—don't forget, we're far more suspicious of government departments than we are of each other."

"One more thing," I said. "We'd like to return your money now—shall we count it again?"

She looked at us in astonishment.

"I was half-hoping you'd look after it for me."

"We'll do anything to help—" I paused "—anything except look after your money."

"How about tomorrow afternoon?" she asked. "I'll have twice that amount if all goes well."

"Why don't we visit your grandparents again?" I suggested.

"Good idea," she replied, then it suddenly hit her.

"We can't go there tomorrow," she wailed, "we can't go anywhere, anywhere at all, without Zappy."

"Don't worry, dear," comforted Joanna. "We can always take Yoddy for a spin—it'll be nice to ride in a good car for a change."

"That's all I need," said Natasha, "someone to cheer me up."

We handed over the money and she stuffed it in her shoulder bag.

"I'm worried sick about breaking the news to them.

They're bound to be very upset and I hadn't planned to do it until the day we defect, but your suggestion for tomorrow is a great idea. We can kill two birds with one stone—I can leave the money in my room, where I know it will be safe, and I can break the sad news to them afterwards.

"Another advantage is that, when the time comes, I can take a taxi from here, dump my stuff at the farm, collect the money and be on my way before the taxi man realises what's going on. This, by the way, may be sooner than you think—Viktor now says it may be as soon as next week, but I still have to wait until he rings before I know for certain.

"Come on—let's take you to visit to the fleshpots of Moscow. Don't forget that I'm still an Intourist guide— this is what I should be doing instead of all this cloak and dagger stuff."

We piled into Zappy for the last time and Natasha pushed the starter button, then she drove ever so slowly up the ramp—perhaps she was still wondering where to take us.

"Cheer up," I said. "Don't forget, you'll soon be the proud owner of Zappy the Second."

She cruised slowly up and down the street, still undecided.

"I'm sorry," she murmured at last. "Would you mind if I took you to my favourite part of Moscow?—Old Arbat. Parking is easy and they've turned Ulitsa Arbat into a new pedestrian precinct, with quite a few cafes and restaurants. We used to come here when I was a student and we'd sit and talk for ages. This part of Moscow is full of happy memories for me and I'd like to recapture some of them if you don't mind."

"Of course we don't mind—we'd like to hear about your student days."

So Ulitsa Arbat it was, with its Pushkin museum, an elegant blue and white flat, where Pushkin and his new, eighteen-year-old bride lived for a while before they moved to Saint Petersburg, where he challenged someone to a tragic duel over her honour and was fatally injured. He died of his wounds a few days later and their flat in Moscow, where they'd been so happy, had been preserved ever since as a shrine to his memory.

Joanna gazed out of the window. "What a waste," she murmured.

"Russia is full of waste," sighed Natasha sadly; "wasted talent, wasted genius, wasted ideals, millions and millions of wasted people—great people—slaughtered in wars, frozen to death in Siberian prison camps—downtrodden, disease-ridden, inarticulate people, drinking themselves to death to keep out the cold and forget how miserable they are."

"That looks like a nice cafe," I said. "Let's sit down and have a cup of tea and you can tell us all about his poetry."

She was word perfect. She told us all she knew about Alexandr Pushkin, Russia's most famous poet, exiled in 1820 and returning a few years later to write his unique novels in verse, notably *Eugene Onegin* and *The Queen of Spades*, which in themselves represented a massive contribution towards the greatness of the Russian novel.

We sat there for ages, soaking up the late autumn sun, watching it disappear over the horizon.

"Oh, I almost forgot," said Natasha. "Your new itinerary came through today—you leave Moscow on Sunday morning and spend one night in Smolensk and one night in Minsk before you cross into Poland on Tuesday."

"But we don't want to stay in Smolensk and Minsk— we asked the manager to allow us to stay here for another two nights and he said it would probably be all right."

"Unfortunately not. I passed your request to Intourist, but they turned it down. They reminded me that you were only a day late arriving and your three weeks are up on Sunday morning, so that's when you have to leave."

"That's worse than being in the army," I pointed out. "I thought the whole point of being on holiday was to travel around a bit. Our visas don't expire until Thursday. Why can't we spend our last few days doing what we want to do instead of always having to comply with silly rules and regulations?"

Natasha smiled. "Don't forget," she said, "life in the Soviet Union is actually worse than being in the army— we're so frightened of America's nuclear capability that the entire country is still on a war footing. The army is still in charge and they will continue to run our country until our own nuclear deterrent is equal to that of America."

"Isn't that rather ridiculous?"

"Of course, but America is still a very real threat as far as we're concerned and that's why we feel we have to control everything and everyone, especially foreign tourists. We need to know where they are and what they're doing. You too were put under surveillance after your detention in Leningrad docks. You aren't the first to be detained and you certainly won't be the last—and that of course led inevitably to your being turned back at your very first roadblock."

"So that's why they picked on us! We eventually realised that it might have something to do with that, but there was never any proof—and now you tell us! Thanks a lot— we could have done with that information a week ago instead of now, when we're about to leave. Why didn't you tell us earlier?"

"I know now that I should have been more honest with you right from the start, but I felt I didn't know you well enough at first—and by then it was too late because I didn't want to spoil our friendship. I do hope you understand."

"Of course we do—and we're so glad we can sit here and talk about these things—misunderstandings can so easily ruin everything."

She rummaged in her shoulder bag and produced our travel permits and petrol vouchers.

"You won't need permits or anything like this once you're in Poland," she said. "The Poles have been more successful than us in getting rid of the bureaucracy which still strangles the Soviet Union. They have to be careful not to provoke the wrath of the Kremlin, but they're gradually regaining their freedom and we wish them luck. If they succeed, there's hope that things will get better here too."

The petrol vouchers reminded me of something— something important.

"I nearly forgot," I said. "Do you know a garage where I can buy 96 octane petrol?"

"Of course," she replied. "I buy it myself for Zappy— Victor won't let me use anything else."

"How about good quality oil? We've got a spare can, but it's not the right viscosity for Yoddy."

"That's a word. I've never heard before, you're trying to catch me out, aren't you?"

The sun had set and the street lights lent enchantment to this bustling little street. Ulitsa Arbat with all its wonderful memories—memories which she would take with her into exile and which might help her come to terms with her new life, to accept the inevitable sorrow and feelings of hopelessness which affect all those trying to build a new life in a strange country. Perhaps Pushkin had felt like this when he was driven into exile in 1820.

"D'you mind if I park Zappy next to your Yoddy? It's her last night here and she'll be glad of the company."

The two cars, parked side by side, gave me a sudden idea—why hadn't I thought of it before?

"Why don't we transfer all your personal stuff to Yoddy?—you know, the bits and pieces people usually keep in their cars? We can take it all with us when we go to see your grandparents tomorrow."

"Even better," Joanna added, "you can pack up everything you don't need to take with you and deliver that to the farm as well. It will save you time and trouble next week—surely you can live out of a couple of suitcases for a few days?"

"What a splendid idea!" exclaimed Natasha. "There's plenty of room at the farm and it will be less of a worry when the time comes. I only need one suitcase anyway— two suitcases would attract too much attention—and it will save time when I get there in case I have to leave quickly for any reason. I'm really dreading tomorrow evening and having to break the news that Viktor and I are planning to defect. It will be very hard for them to understand why we're leaving them alone after all these

years, but I have to make them realise that we're definitely
going and they won't be seeing us again for a very long
time."

"Good news," she told us the next morning. "The manager
is going to the bank today and he's asked me to look after
his office while he's away. This gives me an ideal
opportunity to ring Viktor without going through the hotel
switchboard. The manager has his own outside line, so
the switchboard can't listen to what we're saying. He's
usually away for an hour or more when he goes to the
bank and this will give us plenty of time to discuss the
final details of our defection.

"We arranged last weekend for me to phone him today
if I hadn't heard from him and, in case anyone is listening
in, I have to start by telling him that I'm coming to collect
my new car on Tuesday, He then says that he has to go
to Gdansk that day, whereupon I say 'what a pity—too
late to change my plans now'."

"That doesn't make sense," I interrupted. "Why go to
see him on the very day he won't be there?"

"How stupid can men be?" said Joanna. "Can't you
see?—this is the only way they can both be in Warsaw
at the same time. Viktor will be returning from Gdansk
and Natasha will be driving to the Zaporozhets' agent in
Warsaw to show them her new car so, if everything goes
according to plan, they'll be off to Sweden with the new
car before anyone knows what's happening."

"Exactly," agreed Natasha. "Now let's go down to the
office and make that phone call."

"Hello—is that the Zaporozhets factory? This is

Comrade Fyodorov to speak to my brother Viktor. Could you put me through to the new car showroom?"

"Bit of a euphemism really," she whispered to us. "It's only an old shed next to the assembly line and it's full of cars which have failed their final inspection—cars which, for various reasons, have been rejected. Viktor is the only one who can deal with them. He patches them up and gives them a test drive, after which they're as good as new—'probably better' as he never tires of saying. His young assistant quite fancies him—they usually have breakfast together and I'd be surprised if they didn't share a lot more than breakfast before they even think of food."

"Hello Viktor, I'm coming down on Tuesday to collect my new car. What's that?—Don't say you'll be away on Tuesday, what a shame!...Sorry, much too late for me to change my plans now, we'll have to meet some other time... . Yes, I'll be arriving about midday, so please make sure my new car's ready to drive away. I have to go to Warsaw afterwards to show it to our new agent—yes, I hear he's in trouble over the allocation of new cars...rich people jumping the queue as usual, I expect, but there, that's capitalism for you! Anyway, must go now—hope we can meet up again soon."

She replaced the phone with a flourish.

"There—that's the last piece of the jigsaw. How about a large vodka before we start packing."

"Just one thing," I asked. "Where have you arranged to meet Viktor in Warsaw?"

"At our friend's house, of course—remember you're going to drop in a note to tell them we're on our way. They already know roughly what's going to happen, but they don't know when. The note will confirm that we'll be arriving separately on Tuesday or Wednesday and would they organise passports and book us, with car, on the first available ferry to Sweden. The passports will cost quite a bit, but, thanks to Henry, we shall have plenty to cover this and pay for our passage to Sweden plus any bribes which may be needed and still leave enough over to start our new lives in Scandinavia."

We joined her for a celebratory Stolichnaya, then we made several journeys with all her things until only a solitary suitcase remained, neatly packed with all that was left of her old life—precious memories that, come what may, she couldn't bear to leave behind. How lucky we were that we would never have to leave our country behind and, with only a single case, venture into the unknown.

Eleven

We stacked everything in Yoddy while we waited for Henry to arrive. Natasha wandered around anxiously. She was almost in tears and I knew she was thinking of the happy times that she and Zappy had spent together.

Joanna, who had a bit of a headache, went back upstairs and, dead on three, a little white Skoda chugged down the ramp and into the car park. Henry was nothing if not punctual.

"Would you like me to stay for a while," I asked Natasha, "just in case?"

"I'd be ever so grateful."

Two men got out and looked around. Henry was one and I recognised the other one as his boy friend at El Cubano—the one who had brought in the kebabs and had stalked out of the kitchen in such high dudgeon His obvious annoyance at being upstaged must have been short-lived—or perhaps, like the Caucasian girls, he had nowhere else to go.

Natasha walked over to greet them and I followed.

"Well, look who's here," said Henry.

"Don't worry, I'm only here to protect her interests," I soothed.

"After what happened on Tuesday," he replied, "it's I who should be protected from your predatory sister-in-law—isn't that so, Basil?"

Basil nodded.

"She made a laughing stock of me—and Basil too. It'll take us years to live it down, won't it, Basil?"

Basil nodded again.

"You nearly left me for good, didn't you, Basil?"

I decided that an explanation might be helpful.

"I must apologise on Natasha's behalf," I said. "She must have got carried away."

"You can say that again—she nearly carried me away and all—I had to fight for my honour, didn't I, Basil?"

Natasha was trying hard not to laugh and, remembering the look on Henry's face as she pushed him through the curtain, I too was having great difficulty in keeping a straight face, but it was no use. She started to giggle and we both exploded with laughter. She ran over to Henry and gave him a hug and it was then that I knew she'd manage all right without any help from me. These Russians obviously had their own way of doing things. What on earth was the use of planning anything in advance when they continually ignored the rules and behaved in such an irresponsible manner? How could they ever expect to do business together if they hugged one another before they'd even started?

This was no way to carry on.

First, we should have counted the dollar bills, then they should have made a thorough inspection of Zappy to ensure she was in reasonable working order and had at least a sporting chance of surviving the rigours of the Russian winter and both parties should have signed a declaration to this effect, and then—and only then—should the appropriate documents be produced and receipts obtained. The keys could then be handed over as final proof of ownership and only then, if considered absolutely necessary, the hugging could commence.

Natasha finished her cuddle and looked at me.

"No use looking at me like that—don't forget, I would have slept with the man if he'd wanted me, then you really would have had something to complain about."

"I'm not complaining," I countered, "but I do feel rather superfluous at the moment."

"Sorry about that, but don't forget, we Russians haven't much to laugh about these days and one of the things that keeps us going is our sense of the ridiculous. Thank goodness we can have a good cuddle from time to time without people like you passing judgement on everything we do."

Henry produced a hip flask and we passed it round. I didn't feel much like gulping vodka at that particular moment, but, to avoid further reprimand, I took a hefty swig and the others applauded—the Englishman was human after all.

Things got a bit confused after that.

We staggered over to the Skoda and Henry dragged Natasha inside.

"Time to count the dollarsh," he slurred.

I took Basil to have a look at Zappy, then he asked for the keys and started up. He seemed fairly confident, so we did a few circuits round the car park and I was impressed—at least he was capable of driving home if necessary.

We returned to the Skoda to find them both asleep. Henry was snoring loudly and Natasha was half-waving a nearly empty bottle. I woke her up and gave her Zappy's insurance documents, which she immediately threw away, so I picked them up and tried to explain how important it was not to throw away registration documents when buying a car.

"I'm not buying the car," she slurred, "I'm shelling it, and, in any case, don't worry about the money—we've counted it between ush and it's all there—fifty dollarsh too much in fact. Ishn't that typical of Henry?—he never manages to get anything right. I tried to give it back, but he wouldn't take it—said I should keep it as a geshture of his appreciation for my not having forshed him to deflower me the other night."

"Wouldn't it have been awful if he'd tried?" said Basil. "He'd never have made it, but the whole thing would have been dreadfully embarrassing—and in my kitchen too."

I was glad Joanna wasn't there—she might not have been amused.

Henry was still snoring, so we woke him up and Natasha did her best to give him the registration documents, but he crumpled them up and threw them away too and it was left to Basil to find them. He sorted the documents and folded them carefully before putting them away in the glove compartment, then the three of us had a final discussion on what still remained to be done before the keys were handed over officially.

We decided that, between us, we had done everything reasonably possible to ensure the legality of the transaction. Insurance remained a problem, but, having handed over the keys, we decided that this was no longer our responsibility. Basil was certainly capable of driving the new car and, when he woke up, Henry would probably be able to drive the Skoda home without causing too much damage.

Joanna and I wondered what would become of them. They were, unfortunately, the sort of people who, sooner or later, were bound to come to the attention of those in authority, so we hoped that Henry's not inconsiderable wealth would see them safely through when the time came.

Natasha gave me a hug as they left and her eyes sparkled: "Thanks awfully for your help, I really don't know what I'd have done without you—I'd no idea that selling cars could be such fun."

She ran upstairs to fetch Joanna, and I drove them to Natasha's favourite garage.

"Look what my friends have brought," said Natasha. "All the way from England."

"What's happened to that old rag bag you usually drive?"

"Oh, I gave her away after your last service, when you practically ruined her."

The garage owner turned to me in despair.

"You see the sort of thing I have to put up with—she torments me night and day."

"I wouldn't mind her tormenting me—especially nights," I added.

"That's quite enough," interrupted Joanna. "We haven't got all day to waste and I'm sure this gentleman hasn't either."

"I'd better tell him why we're here," Natasha suggested, "before we come to blows."

"I really have sold my car," she said, "and I'm buying another one next week."

"Why didn't you offer her to me first?"

"I knew Henry would give me a better price."

"Not that shyster—Henry from El Cubano?"

"The very one—shyster he may be, but I bet he's got more money than you."

"More than likely," shrugged the garage man, "but he'll have to look out from now on. I hear he's on the blacklist and the authorities are having him watched, so he'd better be careful—and his lover boy too."

He turned to me.

"Sorry to keep you waiting, sir—Natasha's to blame for keeping on at me like this."

"Don't worry," I soothed. "She keeps on at us all the time—you'll soon get used to it."

"I expect you're here for petrol, sir—96 octane for that little beauty?"

"Yes please," I said, "and—one more thing—we need some special oil."

"Yes," added Natasha, "Visconti oil."

"She means oil of a suitable viscosity," I explained.

The garage man grinned.

"Let's see what you've got in the sump."

I opened the bonnet and he checked the dipstick.

"Nothing much wrong with that—let's have a look at the service manual."

He pursed his lips and gave a low whistle.

"Racing stuff I see—no good just topping up—either carry on as you are or drain the sump and start again. Switch on a moment so I can listen to the engine."

"Nothing to worry about—she's ticking over nicely— but I can always drain the sump if you insist."

"Could you do it tomorrow?" I asked.

He scratched his head.

"Not sure—we're very busy at the moment and I was hoping to have tomorrow off."

Natasha put something in my hand. I glanced down and saw Henry's fifty-dollar bill.

"Put it on the table," she whispered, "don't say anything—wait till he's not looking and leave it there—Russians will do anything for fifty dollars."

He scratched his head again.

"Now I come to think of it, I might just be able to fit her in tomorrow morning. How early can you get here?"

"As early as you like—would eight suit you?"

"Perfect. I'll be interested to see what the Japanese are up to—probably doing their best to undermine our own cars."

"That wouldn't be difficult," I replied, then looked down and saw that the fifty had vanished—talk about sleight of hand.

"How long will it take?"

"No time at all, no more than an hour anyway—we've got trucks coming in and out all the time and you'd be surprised at the muck they've got in their sumps. I'll use up your old oil and charge them extra for the quality and I'd be doing them a favour too."

"Thanks a lot," I said. "See you about eight tomorrow."

We drove to Natasha's grandparents by a roundabout route.

"Better avoid the road block if we can," she suggested. "They won't recognise the car, so they'll probably stop us to check our papers. They might even search the car and ask why we have so much luggage. I could probably explain that away, but they're certain to make out a report and the last thing I want at the moment is my name on a report.

"You know well enough by now—you don't need to do anything wrong to be suspected; the mere fact that your name is there is usually enough to cause suspicion and it would be a disaster if I fell at the last fence."

"That reminds me," I said. "What did the garage man mean when he talked about Henry being on a blacklist?"

"Only category three—the least important."

"How about categories one and two?"

"There are, apparently, three main categories—the most serious one for enemies of the state, then the less serious one for criminals and agitators, then undesirables, such as yourselves. Enemies of the state can be arrested on sight and sent to Siberia without trial, whereas criminals and agitators, at least in theory, can demand a trial before being sentenced.

"As for category three, it's a bit of a joke really. Anyone can be considered an undesirable person at any time and it's an open secret that you only need two or three thousand roubles to bribe someone to take you off the blacklist. The main problem is finding out whether you're on the list or not. Even my garage friend didn't know his name was there until some of his best customers stopped coming, so I had a look at the Intourist list of undesirables at our last monthly meeting and, sure enough, there he was. He was so grateful when I told him that he even forgets to charge me for petrol sometimes."

"I don't understand—why should his customers stop coming when they're told (or manage to find out) that his name's on the list?"

"Guilt by association of course—and that's what'll happen to me if you don't get a move on."

We crawled slowly up the hill leading to the farmhouse

and I knew how much Natasha was dreading the moment of truth—the moment when she would have to tell the old couple that they wouldn't be seeing their grandchildren again for a very, very long time.

"Stop as soon as you get round the corner," she said. "I have to decide the best way to break the news so as not to hurt them too much. How I wish they were on the phone! I could have hinted how Viktor and I were becoming increasingly disillusioned with life under the Soviet system and we were thinking of defecting, then they might have been half-prepared for what I'm going to tell them."

"What's the programme?—what would you like us to do?"

"Just be yourselves, but don't go as far as the cottage—stop about fifty metres away—and don't unpack anything yet. They won't recognise Yoddy, but I'll tell them you have to leave on Sunday and you've come to say goodbye."

"They're bound to ask where your own car is."

"I shall just tell them it's gone in for servicing."

I drove on and we parked some distance away, then Natasha got out and walked towards the cottage.

They'd seen us coming and were waiting outside to greet us.

"What a lovely surprise—and your friends as well, what a splendid car they have. We've just made tea, so you've timed it perfectly."

Natasha beckoned to us, so we left Yoddy where she was and joined them inside.

"You realise of course they wouldn't have bothered to come today if I hadn't told them about your wonderful cream cakes."

"Natasha—fancy saying a thing like that."

195

We drank tea and scoffed our cream cakes without any outward signs of anxiety, although Joanna, perceptive as always, had already noticed that Lyudmila, despite her light-hearted banter, was not quite her usual self.

"She knows something's up," she whispered. "I'm sure she does."

Natasha must have realised this too, because, as soon as we'd finished the cream cakes, she looked straight at us—a look that said unmistakably, 'I have to tell them now—immediately'.

Joanna rose to the occasion: "I hope you don't mind, we'd like to give our car a final check before we leave on Sunday—we've a long journey ahead and, while we're here, we'd like to make sure that she's ready for the journey."

"Of course—you're more than welcome—let us know if there's anything you need."

We sat inside the car and Joanna was crying.

In about half an hour, the cottage door opened and Natasha came out, tears streaming down her cheeks. She beckoned to us and I drove Yoddy up to the front door. No one spoke—we just helped her unload her things, carry them into her room and stack them neatly in a corner, then Natasha closed and locked the door and we went to look for her grandparents. They were sitting, hand in hand, in a dark corner of the living room.

Natasha put her key on the table.

"You usually take that with you, poppet."

"Not this time, babushka. I might lose it, then where would I be on Tuesday when I come to say goodbye? Besides, you may like to look through what I've left to see if there's anything else I might need to take with me."

That was her way of emphasising the awful truth—that

there was no turning back—that she and Viktor were going away for a very, very long time.

It was nearly dark and the five of us sat round the table, sharing our grief, trying to come to terms with the enormity of what was happening.

Nikolai spoke for the first time. He rose to the occasion with a stoicism born of a lifetime of hardship.

"Perhaps we should light a few candles—no point in sitting in the dark."

He got up, but he didn't switch on the light. No one, not even Natasha, would see their grief—that was something he and his dear wife would share together in the years to come. He lit half a dozen candles before he spoke again.

"Perhaps Lyudmila will forgive me if we open her Christmas present now."

He went across to a large corner cupboard and unlocked the door. Natasha joined him and they returned with a huge bottle of Stolichnaya and five glasses.

"On behalf of Lyudmila and myself," he said quietly, "I would like to thank Natasha's friends for their support today. Our beloved daughter died many years ago, but our lovely grandchildren have always been our pride and joy. Now it seems that they will soon be leaving us. May they be happy in the country of their choice and we pray that, in God's good time, they will be able to return for us to bless them before we die."

He poured five glasses and we rose to our feet.

"I give you a toast—to Natasha and Viktor. May they thrive and prosper."

We drained our glasses, then we sat down and waited for him to continue.

"We Russians," he said, "have faced—and still face—

197

hardships which I hope you will never have to endure, but we are a proud and a strong race and our great country is still intact. I am convinced that, sooner or later, our great socialist experiment will eventually prevail, so I give you another toast—Mother Russia."

I have never before, nor since, been as inspired as I was at that moment when, in the flickering candlelight, Natasha's grandfather spoke so lovingly of his country and his faith in the future.

We were up early the next morning to take Yoddy to the garage. A small crowd was already waiting, so the news that a foreign car was coming in for an oil change must have spread rapidly. The proprietor, with an eye for publicity, had obviously made the most of it and there was a ripple of applause when she arrived.

He waved us into the forecourt.

"First of all," he announced proudly, "this magnificent car obviously needs a good wash, then I shall change the oil myself and we will give her a final wash and polish before she leaves."

Ignoring us, he cleared a space on the forecourt and announced that he would permit those who wished to remain to watch the changing of the oil, which of course was an essential part of a car's life.

"It is only rarely," he smiled, "that we are privileged to witness an oil change on such a splendid car and I am proud that my garage has been chosen to carry out this important procedure."

We were beginning to wonder who was paying for what, when he seemed to remember who we were.

"Forgive me," he begged, "I was carried away by my enthusiasm."

"So I see," said Joanna. "You get us here early by telling us you had hoped to take the day off and we find that our car is to be centre-stage for a performance—perhaps all day would suit you?"

He hesitated. It wasn't every day he had a windfall like this. He could already see his photograph in *Isvestia*— what wonderful publicity for the garage. He made up his mind that, regardless of cost, he would keep Yoddy on his forecourt for as long as he possibly could. He was on the point of offering Joanna five hundred roubles for the day when she demanded a free oil change in exchange for the loan of her car—and, of course, he would pay for the oil.

"Of course. I wouldn't dream of charging you anything. Would you like us to keep her here all day?" he asked.

"If you like." Joanna nodded. "We'll call back this evening."

"Congratulations," I said to her, "you've driven a good bargain."

"I'd have done better if I'd had more time to think. Did you see the gleam in his eye when I asked him if all day would suit him?—it was intended as sarcasm, but it obviously backfired. Never mind—it won't cost us anything at all now and we've got the rest of the day for sightseeing."

She consulted her guidebook.

"Let's go and see Ivan—he's not far away."

"Ivan who?"

"The Great Bell Tower, built in 1505. Boris Goudunov, one of the Tsars, added a third storey in 1600 and it became the tallest building in Moscow. It contained twenty-one bells and the largest one was tolled three times whenever a Tsar died. One of his successors commissioned an even larger bell, but this fell from the bell tower and shattered in 1701 and its replacement, weighing an unbelievable two hundred tonnes, was still in its casting pit when the Kremlin caught fire in 1737 and cold water was poured over the bell to protect it from the flames. This caused a large section to break off and this is still displayed at the foot of the tower beside the bell itself, affectionately known as the Tsar Bell and still the largest bell in the world."

Our next port of call was the Cathedral of the Annunciation. This too was destroyed by fire in 1547—in fact, we were astonished to read how many famous buildings were either totally or partially destroyed by fire in the sixteenth, seventeenth and eighteenth centuries. Joanna was particularly impressed at the dedication of the Tsars and the Russian Orthodox Church, who, over three centuries, went to so much trouble and expense to rebuild Moscow's heritage, although I couldn't help reminding her that an efficient fire brigade would have been much more sensible.

We wandered from one splendid building to another, half wishing we were staying for another week. There was so much we hadn't seen—the Moscow Conservatory, the Old University, the Gorky and Chekhov Museums, Pushkin Square and so on—the list was endless.

"We must go to the Bolshoi again," said Joanna. "Tomorrow is our last chance and it's high time we atoned for our bad behaviour the other night—fancy walking out on Stravinsky."

I had to agree with her, there was no possible excuse for what we'd done.

"Never mind. If we hadn't sneaked out," I pointed out, "we wouldn't have gone to Henry's cafe again and I'd never have thought of telling Natasha he might be able to help her sell her car—and you know what that led to."

"Don't we just? Anyway, I've just seen a poster advertising *Spartacus* tomorrow night. It's by Khachaturian—Aram Khachaturian from Armenia. Does the name ring a bell, by any chance?"

It did indeed.

"You don't mean Aram Kuryokhin—your lover boy on the *Pushkin*?"

Joanna bridled and her face flushed.

"Don't you dare call him that—I'd have to be pretty desperate before I'd have anything to do with that creep."

I hastily changed the subject.

"Why don't we carry on to the Bolshoi now and see if we can book for tomorrow?"

"Good idea—we could buy a couple of tickets and have lunch upstairs at the same time—remember the moving staircase and the champagne?"

It was quite a long walk, but the thought of lunch spurred us on and, miraculously, the box office was still open.

There were some good seats left and, throwing discretion to the wind, we bought two of their most expensive seats and went upstairs for a ruinously expensive lunch.

The ruinously expensive bit was entirely her fault, but she was unrepentant.

"I enjoyed that," she said afterwards. "It's about time

we had a good spread without having to count the cost—
that's what a holiday should be all about. Besides, Yoddy
has just saved us at least a hundred roubles—remember?"

I'd almost forgotten Yoddy the star, earning money while
we were squandering it. If truth be told, the champagne
had made us quite sleepy, so we decided to call it a day
and walk back to the garage to see how she was getting
on.

We arrived to find a large crowd and two burly police
officers from the Moscow security police.

"I wonder what they're doing here?" said Joanna.

"Enjoying themselves, by the look of it."

They were indeed entering into the spirit of things,
keeping the crowds back in an orderly and friendly
manner.

The garage owner saw us coming. He rushed towards
us and shook us warmly by the hand before introducing
us to the police officers.

Introductions over, he lowered his voice:

"I need to know your names, just in case."

"Just in case of what?" asked Joanna.

"In case they ask—I told them you were my friends
from England."

"What's that got to do with it?" I asked.

"Obstruction," he said. "Obstructing the highway is a
serious offence and I've had to pay a fine (or, to be more
accurate, a bribe) to avoid being prosecuted, the bribe
being a donation towards their welfare fund in recognition
of their help in controlling a small crowd, which might
otherwise have led to a breach of the peace. I've been
caught like this before—there is of course no welfare fund
and the donation goes into their own pockets. There's

nothing anyone can do about it except smile and give them what they ask for.

"Pity you didn't arrive earlier—the photographer from *Moscow News* has only just left and I'm hoping they'll give us some good publicity. That's why I wanted your names—newspapers always want names before they publish photographs.

"Oh—I nearly forgot—your friend Henry arrived about an hour ago. He was driving Natasha's Zaporozhets and I expect he'll keep her now. I warned him he was on the latest blacklist and he was most grateful—said he'd do something about it right away. He's not short of a rouble or two, so I expect he will. He's quite a decent chap really, so I told him the going rate was between two and three thousand. He asked me to give you his best wishes for your journey home. He's a strange chap, but I quite like him—perhaps he'll become a regular customer."

Twelve

We met Natasha for breakfast the following morning.

"Good news—I told Intourist I was going to Brest Litovsk next week to collect my new car and, as I hoped, they told me all about our new Zaporozhets' agent in Warsaw. They suspected he was fiddling his waiting list in favour of wealthy businessmen instead of Communist-nominated government officials. They gave me a special pass for Poland so that I could go and show him my new car and, at the same time, find out what was happening and report back direct to them.

" 'No need to tell our people in Brest Litovsk,' they said. 'Someone there might be in league with him.'

"This of course is just what I'd been hoping for, so the coast is now clear for me to go on to Warsaw without even having to ask them."

She finished her coffee.

"Perhaps we should write that note now for you to give to my friends in Warsaw, carefully worded of course, but they can read between the lines and they already know what's going on. You should be in Warsaw by Tuesday afternoon, so please deliver this note to them as soon as you arrive. It's strange to think that, if all goes well, I shall be in Warsaw myself that evening, although it's best if we don't meet—too much at stake."

"The Hotel Warsava is in the main square and, if you

can afford it, you really should spend a couple of days there—it's a lovely city, not so depressing as East Berlin, and the hotel itself is splendid—virtually a capitalist paradise. They've already got the makings of a free market economy and the authorities are almost human. They're restoring the old houses and the other buildings in the square as nearly as possible in their original style. They still have a long way to go, but the architects are giving their services and half the workforce are volunteers."

"Do people volunteer here in Moscow?"

"Yes, given half a chance, but we are less motivated here. We're disillusioned with the way things are going and we certainly have no love for the authorities, so why should we bother?"

We went upstairs to compose a suitable note for her Warsaw friends.

It took Natasha some time to get it right, but it was ready at last—full of information, but written in such a way that, if it were found or mislaid, no one would be incriminated.

"Brilliant!" I exclaimed. "What hope is there for bumbling bureaucrats when you're on the war path?"

"Now," said Natasha, "I'll help you pack, else you'll never get away tomorrow—I'd really love to come to the ballet with you tonight, but it's obviously better for us not to meet too often from now on. I hope you enjoy *Spartacus*, though you may find some of the music rather discordant. It's not all blood and thunder—in fact, the love scenes between Spartacus and the slave girl are really beautiful and full of the most romantic music you could ever imagine. I'm sure you'll always remember this evening as a fitting climax to your last day in Moscow."

We finished packing and Joanna thanked her for her help.

"Don't be silly," said Natasha. "You've made such a difference to my life, too."

She suggested that we spent our last afternoon in the park.

"Chess is our national game," she told us. "Everyone plays chess in the park, even in winter. The chess tables overlook the hot springs, which, believe it or not, are warm enough for bathing all the year round. In January, when the water freezes, old men dig holes in the ice to catch fish for their supper."

"The park is a huge open space right in the middle of Moscow and it's only ten minutes walk from here. Children bring fir trees to the park in December and everyone lends a hand with the decorating—they know that the true spirit of Christmas lies in sharing what you have and children are taught by example what sharing means. They run from tree to tree with their presents, not minding who gets them. This, we feel, helps them share more readily when they grow up. If only we realised that this is the true spirit of Communism, not the heavy-handed bureaucracy which blights our lives—but enough of that. What time do you plan to leave tomorrow?"

I looked at Joanna.

"No good looking at me—you're the one who usually decides, so it's up to you."

"I'm still waiting," Natasha laughed.

"Waiting for what?"

"Look, it's high time I went back to my spying before anyone gets suspicious."

"Of course, you have to write your final report—you'd better say nice things about us or we won't deliver your letter to Warsaw."

"Do shut up," admonished Joanna. "Tell her what time you want to leave."

"As early as possible," I replied. "How about straight after breakfast?"

A rumble of thunder reminded us that the fine weather wouldn't last forever. We left Yoddy safe and sound in the underground car park, ready for the journey home, and left our overnight bags in our room; then we walked to the park, trying to forget about the black clouds overhead, although the rain still held off.

We had assumed that the park would be almost deserted, but Muscovites are hardy folk and the chess players continued playing—seemingly unaware of the threat from on high. Even the mothers with babies in their prams went on chatting, as though oblivious to anything that might interrupt their afternoon gossip.

We decided to carry on and the storm broke at the very moment we arrived at the theatre. The rain came down in torrents and we ran through the main entrance and upstairs to the restaurant, where, to our surprise, we found a small and obviously distinguished gathering. Speeches were just commencing, so we crept into a corner, uncertain of our credentials. Reassuringly, a waiter brought us champagne and found us two chairs at the back of the room.

"This celebration," he murmured, "is being held to honour Aram Khachaturian, the Armenian composer, who has just been awarded the order of Lenin. I have here a special programme which has been printed in honour of his seventieth birthday. If you would like one, the price is ten roubles."

The cover had a photograph of Khachaturian with his friend—the violinist David Oistrakh, with the wording 'Khachaturian is the right man at the right time, both for Armenia and the Soviet Union. He has successfully imposed Western harmonies on Armenian melodies, but without taming them. We honour him to night with a performance of his ballet *Spartacus*.'

The wording was repeated in four different languages, Armenian, Polish, German and English and the programme contained the history of Spartacus and the story of the ballet, together with photographs of the production and the principal dancers.

We waited until the reception was over, then we took our places in the auditorium. The lights dimmed, the magic commenced, Khachaturian's beautiful music wove its spell and we were back in Leningrad again, enchanted as we had been on our very first night at the Kirov.

We left the theatre in a dream. The rain had stopped and we looked up at the stars. It was a crisp, clear night and we walked hand in hand, savouring our last night in Moscow.

We walked without speaking. So much had happened in such a short time that we felt overwhelmed by it all. We needed time to think before the long journey home.

Joanna was the first to break the spell.

"How about those hunks of men in the sword dance?—wouldn't mind one of those. If anyone tells me ballet dancers are effeminate I'll tell them to shut up. I can't stand stupid people who haven't the slightest idea what they're saying. How dreadful Natasha must feel now that the time has come for her to turn her back on this beautiful city for an uncertain future. We really must visit them in Sweden next year—promise?"

Natasha joined us for a late breakfast. None of us had had much sleep and we didn't know what to say. The manager arrived to say goodbye, but we weren't in the mood for company and it wasn't long before he sensed our sadness.

"Forgive me," he said. "I really shouldn't be here anyway."

Joanna thanked him for all his help and his friendship towards us.

"It's so sad," he sighed. "People come and people go and I never have much chance even to speak to them, let alone get to know them. Natasha is more fortunate and I can see how well the three of you have got on together. I'm sure she'll miss you when you leave this morning, even more than I will."

We shook hands and Joanna gave him a quick kiss.

He looked as though he was going to cry, then he blew his nose and smiled, kissed her hand, wished us a safe journey and walked slowly back to his office.

I picked up our suitcase and went down to the car park.

I unlocked the boot of the car and slid the case into the space I'd left for it, noting with satisfaction that it fitted perfectly. Everything seemed unreal, almost as though I wasn't standing there at all. Perhaps our own quiet, uneventful lives were equally unreal. Why, I wondered, do people go on holiday to have their lives disrupted and their emotions shattered?—perhaps they needed to escape sometimes.

I opened the car doors and waited for Joanna and Natasha to arrive.

They came down the steps slowly, reluctantly. They were holding hands, their fingers entwined. I wound down the windows when I saw them coming, but they seemed to take ages and, not wishing to intrude, I sat in the driver's seat and watched them in my mirror. They paused from time to time and I realised then how much they loved each other.

I felt guilty somehow—almost a voyeur—so I got out of the car and waved. They waved back and, for no particular reason, I felt reassured—everything was as it should be and we would soon be on our way. I greeted them casually, content to wait until it was time to leave. They were the ones who were grieving and it was important not to interrupt their final moments together.

Natasha came over and gave me a kiss and I knew then that I loved her too.

"Thank you for everything," she whispered. "Look after Joanna until we meet again."

I thought of the love scene from *Romeo and Juliet*:

'Good night, good night—parting is such sweet sorrow that I shall say good night till it be morrow.'

Say goodnight, I thought—say it quickly. I'm going to start the car now, so get on with it before we all start crying.

I found myself in the driver's seat and Yoddy was ticking over—her usual gentle, imperceptible hum.

Joanna was in the passenger seat and Natasha was kissing her through the open window—a long, lingering kiss.

"Don't look round," said Natasha. "Don't either of you dare look round or even wave—I couldn't bear it."

I watched myself pull away and accelerate slowly up the ramp and into the open air.

★ ★ ★

It was raining and Moscow was grey and miserable, but Yoddy didn't mind. She threaded her way skilfully through the morning traffic and it reminded me somehow of our first Sunday in Moscow—was it really only three weeks ago?—when traffic was light and pedestrians stopped in the middle of the road to greet each other. Pedestrians were thin on the ground now and we soon found the main road to Minsk and Smolensk.

Thunder pealed and rain cascaded down with increasing ferocity. We headed due west and, as the suburbs receded, blinding flashes of lightning lit up the road ahead. The storm was now all around and the deafening thunder provided a dramatic climax to our Soviet adventure.

I heard again the commanding voice of Natasha's strong, indomitable grandfather when he had spoken a few days earlier of his love for Mother Russia. I now realised that he had spoken for the millions of Russians who shared his belief in the indestructibility of the Soviet Union. He had said that the Russian people had overcome hardships that he hoped we would never experience and he had been convinced that, sooner or later, their great Communist ideals would prevail.

His words had told us so much that was great about the Russian people—a proud and strong race with their convictions still intact in spite of everything they had had to endure.

We'd barely scratched the surface of this huge country, but we'd met people from other countries along the way—people from Siberia, Mongolia, Germany and Sweden as well as European Russians from different walks of life.

We had encountered the good and the not-so-good of Soviet Russia, but, at the end of our journey, we were still hopeful that, given time, the Russian people might yet be able to solve their problems in their own way.

If you travel properly, you never come back the same person. I like to think that, ignorant as we were of the huge country that our Scandinavian friends called 'the bear next door', we had extended the hand of friendship to this uncertain bear at a time when paranoia and hatred prevented so many people from doing just that.

We now know that bears can also be friendly.